The Fruits
of
Their Labors...

**A History of the
California Raisin Industry
Under Federal and State
Marketing Orders**

First Edition

The Fruits
of
Their Labors...

**A History of the
California Raisin Industry
Under Federal and State
Marketing Orders**

By Clyde E. Nef

First Edition

Malcolm Media Press
Clovis, CA

First Edition 1998

Published by:

Malcolm Media Press
P.O. Box 626
Clovis, CA 93613
559-298-6675

Malcolm Media Press is a division of Malcolm Media Corporation,

publishers of *American Vineyard, California Dairy, Central Valley Farmer, Pacific Nut Producer,* and *Vegetables West.*

Printed in the United States of America

iv

ACKNOWLEDGMENTS

It's impossible to list all of the names of those in the California and world dried vine fruit producing and consuming industries who have contributed to my knowledge of this unique commodity. It has been my good fortune to visit areas of the world that otherwise would just be a spot on the map.

Lasting friendships have been my opportunity to develop with California raisin industry representatives, foreign producers, government representatives, and importers and users of California raisins.

The opportunity to write this book came from the challenge from some of these industry leaders to record some of the history of the raisin industry during the period it has operated under Federal and State Marketing Orders. Hopefully this book will meet their expectations.

My career in the raisin industry has been made possible with sacrifice from my wife, Joanne, and children, Kristine, Allan, Bart and Tonya. I could not have accomplished it without them.

Clyde E. Nef

CONTENTS

Part One -- A History

The Chairman's Report, 1951; British Need Raisins; RAC Acts Quickly; Governments Must Agree; Subject to Subsidy; Supplied Raisins During War; Hears Parliament Debate; Calls Upon Mr. Carr; They Like Our Raisins; Sends Message to RAB; *The Chairman's Report, 1952*; Goes to London; Terms Are Lowest Acceptable; Goes to Geneva; Meets German Importers; Protest Is Puzzling; Raisins Must Move; Exports Needs 75,000 Tons; May Buy 10,000 More; Contract Is Signed; Challenges

Part Two -- The Marketing Orders

Part Three -- International Relations

INTRODUCTION

As a retirement project, the author was given the challenge and request to write a book covering the history of the California raisin industry during the years it has operated under Federal and State Marketing Orders. I was not in California nor even aware such programs existed until late in 1961. Upon my arrival and employment with the U.S. Department of Agriculture in the Fresno Marketing Field Office, I soon learned I didn't even know the language of the industry. Consequently, most of what is included in this book for the years 1950-1962 comes from reading minutes, the Chairman's speeches, reviewing statistics, and the verbal history I have been able to recall.

I'm not a fan nor promoter of reading the last chapter of a book first. It has been difficult for me to write this book without overloading it with statistics. So much of the history of the raisin industry is most graphically told through statistics, even though they are probably most uninteresting to many readers. To limit the use of statistics, I have attempted to condense them to a few tables which are located at the end of the book.

I suggest that readers of this book spend some time reviewing the statistical tables before reading the narrative. As you read, you will hopefully get a clearer picture and better understand the reasons for establishing the Federal and State Marketing Orders and implementation of programs authorized by these Orders. These statistical tables presenting grape acreage, grape production, grape utilization, grower prices, raisin production, raisin shipments, etc., tell a story in and of themselves. They certainly give a pictorial base to review and better understand the establishment of marketing orders and implementation of programs to deal with the industry challenges.

The raisin industry is quite unique among marketing orders. The area covered by these orders is essentially limited to the Central and Southern San Joaquin Valley. Although grapes are a perennial crop, the annual production of raisins is impacted by the grape producers' ability to switch the outlet into which they market their raisin variety grape production almost at the last minute. Vineyard conditions and cultural practices have progressed to tractors, power sprayers, drip irrigation systems, etc., but pruning and harvesting of grapes for raisin production is still all done with hand labor.

It has been my good fortune to work with many super people in the raisin industry; the Agriculture Marketing Service and Foreign Agriculture Service of the U.S. Department of Agriculture and the Marketing Branch of the California Department of Food and Agriculture. Many representatives of dried vine fruit producing countries, importers of dried vine fruits in all parts of the world and potential users of California raisins have contributed immensely to my knowledge of the world dried vine fruit industry. To attempt to identify them all would be futile, but hopefully they will accept my thanks for each of their contributions.

It is difficult, even as I write this, to fully comprehend the places I've been, people I've met, and experiences I've had. Hopefully, from this book can be gleaned where we have been, where we are now, and this knowledge can be used to positively affect where we are going.

I hope you enjoy reading this book and obtain a greater appreciation for "wrinkled grapes" and those involved in their production, processing, and distribution.

TIME LINE OF EVENTS

1949	State and Federal Orders implemented.
1951-54	Committee sales of surplus to U.K. and Germany.
1954	Surplus offers to packers for export to designated eligible markets.
1956	Establishment of minimum grade and condition standards and implementation of third party inspection.
1961	First International Sultana/Raisin Conference.
1961	U.S. Government offer of disaster (rain) insurance.
1967	Establishment of Raisin Bargaining Association (RBA).
1970	Swanson Study regarding advertising / promotion.
1971	Increase in State Assessment from $5 to $20 per ton.
1971	Implementation of minimum grade standards for dried vine fruit imported into the U.S.
1971	Resignation of Chairman after 22 years service.
1972	Spring frost.
1976	Harvest time disaster (rain).
1976	Change from reserve offers for export to Export Adjustment Offer Program.
1976	Abolished the Federal Raisin Advisory Board and expansion of the Committee to 47 members and 47 alternates.

1976	Implementation of Trade Demand formula.
1978	Another harvest time rain disaster.
1982	Development and implementation of packer "Credit Back" Program.
1984	Award of "Helms Bill" funds for export advertising/promotion. Subsequently, TEA, MPP, and MAP funds.
1984	Development of "Dancing Raisins" Commercials.
1984	Reduction of free tonnage field price to $700 per ton and implementation of Free Tonnage Adjustment Program.
1984	Development and implementation of the Raisin Diversion Program (RDP).
1994	Termination of the State Marketing Order and California Raisin Advisory Board (CALRAB).
1995	Conversion of export adjustment offers from 100% reserve raisins to 50% raisins and 50% cash.
1996	Conversion of Export Adjustment Program to 100% cash adjustment.
1998	California Raisin Marketing Board (CRMB) formed.

Part One

A History

THE DECADE OF THE 1950's

H istory has proven that the arrival of the 1950's probably did not offer challenges to the raisin industry significantly different from most agriculture commodities. However, how the raisin industry faced and dealt with those challenges was of significant difference.

Agriculture in general and the raisin industry specifically had met the call of the nation's leaders to produce food and fiber to meet the demands of the nation and the U.S. allies during World War II. Now this great demand had ended, but the industry's ability to produce raisins had not. The demand for labor to meet the materials, distribution, and food to support this great effort ended. Soldiers were discharged and returned home. The economies of the U.S. allies as well as those of the surrendered nations were devastated. Now the task of rebuilding must be faced.

Men of vision explored opportunities to save their occupations and build a future. Such men associated with the production, processing, and marketing of raisins learned of legislation approved by the Federal and State governments in the late 1930's which was intended to allow agriculture commodity groups to help themselves. The Federal legislation was the Agriculture Marketing Agreement Act of 1937 and the State legislation, the California Marketing Act of 1937.

One industry leader, who became my mentor, was A. "Sox" Setrakian. "Sox," as he was known in the raisin industry, was an immigrant from Izmir, Turkey. He arrived in the U.S. penniless, became a cable car cleaner in San Francisco, lead the organization of the cable car cleaners union, and put himself through law school. He told me he tried one case in court and as he walked out of the courtroom after successfully defending his client, vowed he would never enter another courtroom as a prosecuting or defense attorney. To the best of my knowledge, that vow was never broken.

Sox became involved in several agricultural endeavors including grape vineyards, table grape production, processing and shipping, raisin production and wine grape production, crushing and wine production. With the conditions in the raisin industry following World War II, he lead the industry's investigation into possible solutions. Several contacts were made by the Chairman with government representatives individually, and as the leader of industry delegations. He became very intrigued with the authority provided in the Marketing Agreement Act and lead many district meetings of raisin producers to explain the proposed raisin marketing order and to solicit their support for such a program.

Pursuant to the authority of the Agricultural Marketing Agreement Act of 1937 and the California Marketing Act of 1937, separate public hearings were held applicable to proposed programs. Separate referendums were conducted and marketing orders made effective in August of 1949. The Federal Marketing Order was implemented to regulate the handling of raisins produced from grapes grown in California. The State program was a Marketing Order for California Raisins, which provided for research, public relations, and advertising/promotion. Both the Federal and State Marketing orders were implemented at virtually the same time. Mr. Setrakian was deeply involved in the implementation and administration of the Federal program, but took no part and expressed limited interest in the State program.

Although both the Federal and State programs are administered by industry representatives and funded by raisin growers and packers, all actions of the administrative bodies have to be approved by the U.S. or State Department of Agriculture. Also these programs were required to be enforced by the U.S. Justice Department or the State Attorney General. Separate staffs employed to administer these programs were hired by those selected to serve on the respective administrative bodies and paid from the industry funds.

The challenge began. Industry representatives had been selected and now faced the challenge to market raisin production in excess of the then known demand. Mr. A. "Sox" Setrakian was elected Chairman of the Federal Administrative body known as the Raisin Administrative Committee (RAC). He served in this position for 22 years, until he resigned on July 1, 1971. With the support of raisin growers and packers serving as the RAC, he began the search for opportunities to dispose of the annual raisin production.

Through contacts with government representatives and elected political representatives, Mr. Setrakian learned of appropriated Federal funds which could be used to subsidize the payment to producers for food exported to the U.S. allies and also citizens of surrendered nations. Sox made many personal visits to Washington, D.C., and several long journeys - some by boat - to London.

Sox met with high ranking representatives of the British Ministry of Agriculture, Fisheries and Food. Negotiations were difficult since nothing like this had been done before. There were no precedents to fall back on. Ultimately agreement was reached under which the U.S. Government would pay part of the grower prices for raisins and the British government would pay the balance. With this agreement in hand, Sox returned to the Committee and began the challenge to put together the terms and conditions necessary to fulfill the negotiated agreement.

Sales of surplus pool raisins were made by the RAC to the governments of Germany and the United Kingdom. The RAC contracted with packers to pack the surplus raisins, arranged for shipping, collected payment from the German, U.S., and U.K. governments, paid packers for processing and distributed the remaining equity to the raisin growers.

Since it took time and effort to develop these sales, 18,844 tons of 1949-50 crop year surplus raisins were sold for livestock feed. The industry recognized the income obtained for surplus tonnage sold for livestock feed was not in the best long term good for raisin growers, and thus supported the Chairman's efforts to sell surplus raisins to designated export markets.

The trips to London, and sometimes Germany and Scandinavia, were challenging and long, often times lasting for over a month. This was a new experience, not only for Chairman Setrakian but also for the government representatives of the United Kingdom. Available funding was at a premium and high level decisions were required to allocate the limited U.S. dollars for the purchase of raisins. These experiences are best recorded for history in two reports the Chairman made to the Committee following the successful completion of purchase agreements. These two reports, one made on December 20, 1951, and the other on November 14, 1952, are included herein in their entirety as they, in considerable detail, reveal the challenges and successful solution.

THE CHAIRMAN'S REPORT
December 20, 1951

Monday, December 10th, Mr. G.W. Baldock, representing His Majesty's government and the United Kingdom Treasury and Supply Delegation, and your Chairman, representing the Raisin Administrative Committee, signed the contract covering the sale of the entire tonnage of raisins in the export surplus pool.

I signed the application to export under the subsidy program. Mr. E.M. Graham approved the application. The sale of the surplus pool raisins was closed and behind us.

I know the press, the radio and the Raisin Industry News have done a good job of reporting this sale.

Notwithstanding, I believe it is necessary and proper that we report to you in detail, step by step, the efforts which were used to bring about a sale which would prove favorable to the raisin industry and the United Kingdom.

The seed for such a sale was planted by the raisin industry's committee last June in Washington, when the committee met Dr. Stedman and his associates in the British embassy.

At that time, the committee stressed the importance of an early purchase by Great Britain of 1951 raisins.

In the middle of August, the subcommittee met Dr. Stedman again. The possibility of an early sale appeared somewhat favorable.

In September, Dr. Stedman advised that the Ministry of Food gave little hope for the purchase of 1951 raisins because of the dollar shortage.

Later that month Dr. Stedman was called to London to assume the office of Under Secretary of the Ministry of Food.

Prior to his departure, Dr. Stedman and I conferred at great length about the possibility of a 1951 raisin sale and he prom-

ised to let us know early in October the thinking of the Ministry of Food.

I telephoned Dr. Stedman in London October 6th. He said there was a great need for raisins but the dollar situation was going from bad to worse. He promised to do all in his power to bring about a purchase. He also promised he would wire soon whether it would be desirable for an authorized representative to visit London and discuss possible business.

On October 8th, we received the following cable from Dr. Stedman: "Can not yet advise whether early visit useful. Will wire further soonest."

Signed "Food Keeper," Dr. Stedman's code name.

On October 10th, Dr. Stedman sent the following cable: "Regret visit now will not prove useful."

BRITISH NEED RAISINS

I telephoned Dr. Stedman October 12th and he said in effect: "Sox, we need raisins. We need them badly. But we are suffering a terrible shortage of dollars. The door for a sale of raisins is not closed but we cannot expect any action now for obvious reasons."

There was nothing to do but hope and wait.

In the latter part of October, I learned that the California Prune and Apricot Growers Association was sending Mr. Jack Gomperts to London to interest the British government in the purchase of a substantial tonnage of California prunes.

I discussed with Mr. Hines the advisability of asking Mr. Gomperts to call on Dr. Stedman and discuss with him the surplus raisin purchase situation.

We agreed that such an approach might prove helpful provided that Dr. Stedman approved such a meeting and also that Mr. Gomperts would act strictly in an unofficial capacity.

I telephoned Dr. Stedman and told him that Mr. Hines and I were planning to ask Mr. Gomperts to visit him and discuss with him the 1951 raisin sales situation provided he approved.

Dr. Stedman believed some good might come from such a meeting and further said he was fond of Mr. Gomperts and had faith in his integrity and judgment.

On November 5th, I received the following wire: "Notwithstanding Churchill's speech Tuesday and Butler's Wednesday stressing greater austerity, less food, less imports, Stedman fighting hard for 20,000 long tons and feels slightly better than even chance of success. Stedman specifically requests absolutely, positively no publicity, not even discussion with anybody, repeat anybody, until decision made, as slightest leak might upset whole applecart." Signed: "Jack."

Soon after receiving this wire, I contacted Dr. Stedman and was happy to learn that they might need more than 20,000 long tons. He did, however, make it definitely clear that while they needed raisins very badly, yet the squeezing of enough precious dollars for the purchase was a tough job.

Dr. Stedman also said: "Sox, we are doing all possible so as to purchase raisins but we are not sure. If the slightest publicity is given to the anticipated purchase and the deal does not materialize, we will have given rise to a lot of false hopes and that sort of thing should be prevented by all means."

From November 5th to November 20th, Mr. Gomperts kept us posted almost daily by cable and telephone on developments regarding the possibilities of effecting a sale. I telephoned Dr. Stedman and Mr. Gomperts several times during these 15 days, and each time the prospect of making a sale looked a little brighter, but not sure.

On November 19th, Mr. Gomperts sent the following cable:

7

"Stedman called to the Treasury for meeting tonight. Keep your fingers crossed."

Tuesday at 1 p.m. arrived Stedman's wire which said:

"Ministry would welcome visit of authorized representative of RAC to discuss possibility of business."

> *Signed: "Food Keeper."*

RAC ACTS QUICKLY

At long last, the wire had come. There was not a moment to lose. Each day counted. The RAC Executive Committee met the same day at 7:30 p.m. and directed me to proceed to London at once and drafted the following letter for me to present to Dr. Stedman:

"Dr. Ralph Stedman, Ministry of Food,
United Kingdom, London, England
Dear Sir:

We have received your wire of November 20. We have directed Mr. A. Setrakian, the Chairman of the Raisin Administrative Committee, to proceed to London to discuss with the proper authorities the possibility of the sale of 1951 raisins.

Mr. Setrakian has been given full authority to act for the Raisin Administrative Committee.

> *Sincerely,*
> *RAC Executive Committee*
> *By: Walter K. Hines,*
> *Vice Chairman"*

I left San Francisco the following morning and arrived in Washington Thursday. Mr. S.R. Smith and Mr. E.M. Graham took time out from their Thanksgiving festivities and reviewed the situation and hoped that a sale helpful to the raisin industry and Great Britain would be made.

I boarded the plane Friday, November 23, at 4 p.m. and ar-

rived at the London Airport Saturday at 9:10 a.m.

Mr. John Scouler, Director; Mr. Charles Parsons, Deputy of the British Dried Fruit Division, and Mr. Gomperts had done the raisin industry the honor of meeting me at the airport.

Dr. Stedman joined us soon after our arrival at the hotel and we discussed the raisin situation in a friendly atmosphere.

After a brief visit, I was directed to meet the Ministry of Food officials Monday, November 26th, at 10 a.m. in Dr. Stedman's office to talk possible business.

At that meeting were Dr. Ralph Stedman, Undersecretary acting as chairman; Mr. Scouler, Mr. Parsons, and Edward Harmer, Esq., representing Finance.

Mr. Scouler asked: "What is the tonnage of raisins which the Raisin Administrative Committee can sell?" I said, "All indications are that the export surplus pool will contain approximately 30,000 short tons and we would be glad to discuss the sale of the entire tonnage, provided, however, that if the tonnage fell short, the Raisin Administrative Committee would be held free from any liability."

Dr. Stedman then asked: "Assuming that the export pool contains more than 30,000 tons or if the Raisin Administrative Committee decides to divert more raisins into the export pool, would the Raisin Administrative Committee give the United Kingdom the first call for the purchase of such additional tonnage?"

I answered, "I believe the Raisin Administrative Committee would give the United Kingdom the first call up to 10,000 additional tons."

Dr. Stedman then said: "What is the price which the Raisin Administrative Committee will want?"

I said: "Gentlemen, this is a question which I can answer easily. I have received a cable from the Executive Committee of the Raisin Administrative Committee directing me as to the price which should control the sale. May I read the cable:

"Executive Committee met today to further discuss your mission to London. Movement of raisins to competitive countries reasonably good. We have carefully considered price which should govern sale of raisins to United Kingdom. After thorough study and survey, cost processing, shrinkage, dock charges, have concluded that price controlling sale to United Kingdom should be one hundred fifty-five to one hundred sixty dollars per ton. This price plus subsidy growers will realize approximately one hundred sixty dollars per ton. As you know, RAC offered to sell for school lunch basis would net growers one hundred sixty-one dollars fifty cents per ton. Later when government offered to purchase at lesser price, RAC regretfully turned down government's counter offer. Obviously we should sell only at price where grower would be able to realize approximately one hundred sixty dollars per ton. We appreciate your services and extend to Stedman and his associates our high regards. Signed: Walter G. Rice, Forrest Farrar, Walter K. Hines."

Dr. Stedman said, "We were hopeful that we would be able to purchase at a somewhat lower price than you have indicated."

I said, "Gentlemen, everyone on the Federal Raisin Advisory Board is most anxious to be helpful to the United Kingdom and for that very reason, I shall assume the responsibility of shaving $2.50 per ton and agree to sell the entire tonnage on a basis of $152.50 f.a.s."

GOVERNMENTS MUST AGREE

The conference for the sale of the surplus raisins lasted almost an hour. We agreed as to price, tonnage, payment, delivery and other essential features, subject of course, to the approval of the United Kingdom Treasury, Minister of Food, the United States

Department of Agriculture, and the Raisin Administrative Committee. Last Monday I was advised that the Treasury and the Ministry of Food have approved the purchase of 27,500 long tons, equal to 30,800 short tons. I telephoned Mr. Graham and Mr. Hines and told them what had developed. They both thought the sale would prove highly satisfactory and helpful.

Tuesday, I was directed to contact Mr. Graham and Mr. Hines and request that no publicity be given to the sale because the Minister of Food most likely would desire to make the announcement personally Thursday.

I sent to Mr. Graham and Mr. Hines the following cable: "Food Ministry requested today that purchase of raisins not be publicized until Thursday when Minister will make announcement here."

Somehow, the news of the sale had leaked out. I suggested that a cable containing all the conditions be sent without delay for the study and decision of the Raisin Administrative Committee. I drafted a cable which, boiled down, contained the following:

1. *RAC agreed to sell and the United Kingdom agreed to buy 27,500 long tons or 30,800 short tons a basis of $152.50 per short ton, f.a.s.*

2. *That if the tonnage of raisins in the surplus pool proved shorter that RAC would be held free from any liability.*

3. *That in the event the export surplus pool should contain tonnages larger than 30,800 short tons, the United Kingdom would have the first call for the purchase of such additional tonnage up to 10,000 short tons.*

4. *That the United Kingdom would have ample funds in any bank which the RAC would designate for the prompt payment of raisins upon the presentation of the required shipping documents.*

I read the cable to Mr. Hines. He suggested that I add the provision making it clear that raisins sold to U.K. were not to be resold to another country.

This provision was added to the cable. Dr. Stedman studied the cable and gave his approval and it went on its way.

On Wednesday, Dr. Stedman drafted a short memorandum concerning the sale. This was to be signed by him for the Ministry of Food and by me for the Raisin Administrative Committee.

I requested that the signing of the memorandum be deferred until I had been advised of the RAC's decision.

The RAC's answer to my cable arrived Thursday. It was a fine message and I am grateful for it.

SUBJECT TO SUBSIDY

The RAC's message contained an essential point which I had overlooked. This was that:

"The sale is subject to the approval of government's current subsidy on Natural Thompson raisins, namely $55 per ton."

Copies of the RAC's cable were given to Messrs. Stedman, Scouler, Parsons, and Harmer.

The deal was closed with the understanding that the RAC would draft a contract as soon as possible in line with the conditions covering the sale as outlined in the cable for the execution of the United Kingdom and the Raisin Administrative Committee. This report would be incomplete if I failed to report to you the swell job done by Mr. Gomperts during his three weeks stay in London. He kept us posted almost daily by cable and telephone and served the raisin industry loyally and effectively.

Now a word or two about my stay of seven days in London. I shall never be able to pay my debt of sincere thanks and gratitude to Dr. Stedman, Mr. John Scouler, and Mr. Charles Parsons, who went out of their way to make my stay in London enjoyable, interesting, and comfortable.

Tuesday, His Majesty's Government had arranged a luncheon. Sir Albert Feaveryear, Deputy Minister of Food, was the chairman. Others present were Undersecretaries Frank Hollis, Ralph Stedman; Director Schouler, Deputy Director Parsons; Edward Harmer, Esq., Gilbert H. Carr, Commander of the Most Honorable Order of the British Empire, Jack Gomperts, your Chairman, and others.

We drank toasts to the King and the President of the United States. We lunched in the most cordial, friendly and congenial surroundings. During the luncheon, Sir Albert said: "Sox, about three weeks ago, we almost gave up hope of being able to invite an authorized representative to visit London and discuss business with us.

Fortunately, we were able to cut here and there and make available enough dollars for the purchase of the tonnages of raisins involved. Please tell the raisin industry we are appreciative of its approach in completing this deal in such a short time because we really need the raisins.

We like California raisins and we like to do business with you people. I have no doubt that the present pleasant relationship will be continued. We are having hard times. We have had hard times before. We have always pulled through and in God's good time we will pull through again."

I answered, "Sir Albert, naturally we are glad that we have been given the privilege of selling a substantial tonnage of raisins to Great Britain, because such a sale will prove to be of great help to the raisin industry. But that which makes all growers and packers most happy is the thought that in these dark days, perhaps we are able in some small measure to be helpful to the *heroic people of this great country, Great Britain.*

SUPPLIED RAISINS DURING WAR

During the terrible war years of 1943 and 1944, the raisin growers wrote the most brilliant chapter of loyalty and sacrifice in the history of American agriculture when they produced in those two years the huge tonnage of 707,000 tons of raisins. We the raisin growers were happy to produce raisins because we knew at that time that substantial tonnages of our raisins were being supplied to our overseas allies, especially to the heroic people of Great Britain.

Today we are again profoundly happy that we can supply Great Britain with raisins because we feel that our raisins, perhaps in some small measure, will lighten the burden of food rationing which weighs so heavily upon the backs of the British people.

Sir Albert, we, the members of the raisin industry pledge our sincere and wholehearted cooperation whenever the occasion may arise. With a heart full of humility, may I thank you and your colleagues for the spirit of kindness, sympathetic understanding, and friendship which all of you have manifested so generously. God bless you all."

Wednesday I had the privilege of meeting with the heads of the various warehouses where the raisins will be stored. I was indeed proud to learn that our raisins are considered and accepted as the best.

The raisin growers were complimented for growing the best quality and the packers for their skill and know-how in packing and delivering the cleanest and most eye appealing raisins in the world.

Thursday, Dr. Stedman and I attended the luncheon of the United States Chamber of Commerce of London as the guests of

14

the luncheon's chairman, Mr. Gilbert H. Carr.

Thursday, it was my good fortune to meet Mr. Stanley Powell of California Packing Corporation in London. Stanley was mighty well pleased. He believed the sale would contribute much to the stability of the raisin industry and help to restore trade confidence.

HEARS PARLIAMENT DEBATE

Thursday evening we attended Parliament to hear the debate on Christmas food supplies. For years the government has been giving the people additional food rations for Christmas. The government had decided there would be no additional food rations for the coming Christmas.

Mrs. Jean Mann of the Opposition Party rose and presented the following resolution, "That the House deplores the decision of the Government not to issue any additional food rations at Christmas." She was a powerful speaker, blending her talk with humor and bitter sarcasm. She attempted to place the responsibility of food shortages and the strictest kind of rationing on the doorstep of the Conservative Party. She condemned the Tories who wooed the British womanhood with false promises to win the election, and said: "Never since the episode in the Garden of Eden were women so assiduously wooed and courted. The blandishments and the dulcet tones with which we were addressed makes the great screen lover Charles Boyer but a clumsy lout."

Miss Ward from the Conservative Party took the floor and said: "For the purpose of historical accuracy, I want to suggest to the Honorable Lady that it was Eve who wooed Adam and not Adam who wooed Eve."

Mrs. Mann replied: "I would refer the Honorable Lady to the first chapter of the greatest Book in all literature, and I think she will understand the analogy was not Adam but the serpent."

Speaker after speaker attacked the Government's decision. At last the time had come for the Minister of Food, Major Lloyd George, to defend the Government's position. He is tall and soft spoken and presented the Government's case calmly, without passion, and used logic which seemed sound and unchallengeable. He said: "If the honorable members of the Opposition had faced up to the situation, things would have been different today and they must realize it is not a question of Christmas bonuses which are involved but the very rations themselves which may be in danger. The fact of the matter is that the honorable members of the Opposition have deluded the electorate for so long they have now succeeded in deluding themselves. We as a nation are not earning enough at this moment to give us all the good things which we want. We are bound to be in difficulties in getting the things we want and particularly the food we want, and it is an especial tragedy that our position here should be so worsening that we have not only to curtail imports from dollar areas but from Sterling areas as well, particularly from our traditional markets in Europe."

Speakers from both sides upheld and attacked the resolution. Finally the resolution was defeated, Ayes 264, Noes 301.

The night was gradually wearing away. We left, admiring the gallant people of Great Britain who suffer the pains of austerity year in and year out and say with a smile: "Yes, it is a bit rough, but in God's good time we will pull through."

Friday was rather a crowded day. It was the day to thank those who had been so gracious, so helpful and bid them "Goodbye."

CALLS UPON MR. CARR

I called upon Gilbert H. Carr first. Mr. Carr represents the

Sun Maid interests in London. He is the president of the United States Chamber of Commerce of London and is very well thought of, received and respected by everyone. The Sun Maid management and the membership can be proud of having a man like Mr. Carr in charge of their interests in England. His assistant, Mr. McKnight, is very well thought of also. Mr. Carr was very happy that the sale was concluded. He said: "For the first time in many years, the English markets are completely out of California raisins. The sale will help to improve the diet of the English people. Raisins are one food item the English housewife can hardly do without."

Mr. Carr asked me to extend his high regards to growers and packers. I thanked him for all he had done for us, knowing that in Mr. Carr, the raisin industry has a good and loyal friend.

Then I called upon Mr. John Scouler and Mr. Charles Parsons. Mr. Scouler is an Australian, and the head of an Australian cooperative association. His services have been loaned to the government. Mr. Parsons also is an executive of a cooperative association and his services are loaned to the government.

These two men are charged with the responsibility of obtaining the needed dried fruits from the world markets. They expressed the hope that the existing pleasant relationship between His Majesty's Government and the raisin industry will be maintained, continued and preserved. They requested that no stone be left unturned for prompt delivery of raisins.

THEY LIKE OUR RAISINS

I pledged them our complete cooperation. Mr. Scouler and Mr. Parsons said they like our raisins and hope that the dollar situation may improve to a degree where they will be able to purchase large quantities of California raisins each year.

I thanked them for their attitude of helpfulness and sympa-

17

thetic understanding and bid them "Goodbye."

Friday noon I received an invitation from the Minister of Food, Major Lloyd George, to pay him a visit.

Dr. Stedman and I met the Minister, who is the son of the former Prime Minister who rendered such distinguished service during World War I. The Minister regretted very much that the purchase had not taken place at a time when the British housewives would have some raisins for Christmas and hoped that we would do all possible to rush the shipments.

I told him, "Mr. Minister, I know I speak for each and every packer when I say to you that we will give the British shipments priority. We not only promise but pledge to you that every ship will be loaded on schedule. We will not let you down."

He seemed so much relieved and said, "We appreciate what you people did for us last year, and we are very much pleased that the present purchase was concluded without delay. We hope that we may be able to purchase a lot of raisins from you people in the years to come. We need you, you need us, and there is no reason why the present pleasant relationship should not be maintained."

I replied, "Mr. Minister, of course last year's and the present sale of raisins contributed a great deal to the stability of our industry. We are grateful that we are given the opportunity to do business with His Majesty's Government. Might I say we are happy. During the terrible war years of World War II, raisin growers produced huge tonnages of raisins and served the war effort well because large tonnages of those war years' production were sent overseas to our allies, especially to our great and gallant ally, Great Britain.

Today, we are happy again, most happy, and have the spiritual satisfaction that the raisins which we have sold to you, per-

haps in some small measure, will help to improve the diet of the good people of this great country.

Mr. Minister, I know I speak for every grower and packer when I say to you that you can depend on us."

We talked about his good father, Former Prime Minister, David Lloyd George, who had been not only a staunch friend of the Armenians but a gallant fighter for the independence of all oppressed nations.

I thanked the Minister and said goodbye to a great man who is doing a good job for his country.

Late Friday I called to say goodbye to Dr. Ralph Stedman. This visit was a happy climax for a happy mission.

Never in my life have I met a man who has personified the good virtues of integrity and fair play in a larger measure than Dr. Stedman. He has very high regard for those serving on the Federal Raisin Advisory Board and the Raisin Administrative Committee. He is a good friend of ours. Dr. Stedman said: "Well, Sox, now that the deal is closed and the RAC has approved your cable, will you please sign this short memorandum so that we can have some evidence of the purchase."

I signed the memorandum. Here it is:

"I confirm the agreement which we agreed on Tuesday, 27th November, concerning the purchase from the Raisin Administrative Committee of the entire tonnage of 1951 crop of Thompson Natural Seedless Raisins in the export surplus pool, estimated to be 30,000 short tons basis $152.50 per short ton f.a.s.

This purchase is subject to the approval of Government's current subsidy on Natural Thompson Seedless Raisins, namely $55 per short ton.

We should also like to have first offer of any further supplies up to 10,000 short tons which might be available in the export surplus pool.

We agree that if the export surplus pool tonnage proves to be less than 30,000 short tons the Raisin Administrative Committee will be held free from any penalty for short delivery.

We understand the Raisin Administrative Committee will forward to us as soon as possible an agreement containing the details necessary for the proper and timely delivery of the tonnage of Natural Thompson Seedless Raisins purchased from the Raisin Administrative Committee.

Immediately after we have received the agreement, we will execute copy and send it back to the Raisin Administrative Committee.

We should like to have 15,000 tons of this quantity shipped as quickly as possible, the balance to be shipped as soon as this can conveniently be done.

Please accept my thanks and that of my colleagues for the understanding which you displayed when we explained the problems which confronted us and for the consideration which enabled us to reach agreement without long drawn out discussions."

SENDS MESSAGE TO RAB

Dr. Stedman gave me a short note and requested that I read it at our first Board meeting. Here is the note: "My dear Sox:

I need not emphasize how much I appreciate all that you and your Committee and the Government of the USA have done to facilitate this agreement. I remember so well the happy time I spent with you and with your colleagues in California. I remember saying then that raisins were one of the things for which we should always try hard to spare dollars. I hope and trust that as the years pass, our dollar difficulties gradually dissolve - but they are certainly going to be with us for some time to come, howsoever busily we export and howsoever austerely we fare at home!

May I mention the help which Mr. Gomperts extended to me when we were struggling to lay the foundations for this transaction. It was a pleasure to have him with us and we look forward, not only to seeing him, but others of our California friends from time to time.

I should not like to close this letter without saying how much we have enjoyed having you in our midst in this great Capital city or without wishing you well on your return to California. With kind regards and all good wishes, as ever, "Ralph."

The time had come to say good bye to a good man. I thanked him for all that he had done for us and hoped that he would visit us in California in the not too distant future.

My mission had come to an end. I obtained the first available passage and left London for home. I left with a heart full of admiration for the gallant British people whose love for and loyalty to their great country has neither bound nor limit. They are resolved and determined to pull through, and God willing, they will.

I am thankful and grateful that I was given the opportunity to serve.

THE CHAIRMAN'S REPORT
November 14, 1952

(The following report was read by Chairman A. Setrakian at a joint meeting of the Federal Raisin Advisory Board and the Raisin Administrative Committee in Fresno, California.)

My Friends:

It is good to be back. It is good to be with you. I know the excellent job which the radio, the press, and the Raisin Industry News have done in reporting the recent sale of the 1952 surplus raisins.

Notwithstanding, I believe it is proper that we report to you in detail the efforts which were used to bring about the kind of a sale which would prove helpful to the raisin industry and the United Kingdom.

GOES TO LONDON

Soon after the frost danger was over and it was evident that the 1952 raisin crop would be substantially larger than that of 1951, your Chairman was directed to go to London and, if necessary, to other friendly countries in Europe and see what could be done toward exporting substantial tonnages of 1952 raisins, and try to sell some 1951 surplus raisins.

We met on June 27th. I said: "There is a great and active need for our raisins in England and the friendly areas of Europe."

I read the letter of Undersecretary Ralph E. Stedman. Mr. Stedman said: "I cannot say more than I have said from time to time in the past. Namely, that both on grounds of quality and price, the United Kingdom continues to be a potential buyer."

This, and other similar statements made by the Ministry officials made us feel that the prospects for the sale of some 1952 raisins to the United Kingdom appeared promising.

We wrote to Mr. Charles Parsons of the Ministry of Food

under date of June 2nd and pointed out the mutual advantages of an early sale. Mr. Parsons answered under the date of July 5th and said: "I could not agree more when you say that an early purchase, by the Ministry, of California raisins will be advantageous to us. We are working hard to this end and I am not unhopeful that we shall eventually be permitted to make a deal."

We were in constant touch with the Ministry of Food. Reports indicated that the general economic position of the United Kingdom showed signs of continuing improvement and there was hope that the improvement might be accelerated.

With the passing of each day, the prospects of selling a large tonnage of surplus raisins to the United Kingdom looked brighter and brighter. The possibility of such a sale encouraged us to tell the growers to make raisins.

While we felt we were taking a chance, yet, because of the fact that we knew the prices controlling all varieties of grapes delivered to the wineries would be starvation prices, there was nothing else we could do but to encourage the making of raisins and hope for the best.

The grower members of the Federal Raisin Advisory Board did a magnificent job of keeping in touch with the raisin growers and helping them to plan in time and not get caught in a squeeze if they intended to make raisins.

In mid-August there was left no doubt that the 1952 raisin crop would be large. We knew that unless we succeeded in selling a large tonnage of surplus raisins to the United Kingdom in September, if possible, but not later than the early part of October, the raisin growers would be forced to sell their raisins at disastrously low prices. We redoubled our efforts. We pleaded with the United Kingdom for an early purchase of raisins if at all possible.

The first break came on August 25th. We received the following wire from the Ministry of Food: "Regarding your inquiries possibility Ministry purchase California raisins: First, still under review and present prospect not too encouraging; second, there are, however, indications of improvement in economic position and we hopeful may be permitted commence negotiations toward end September; third, in such an event in view of large crop would expect very attractive prices.

Signed: Food Keeper."

We kept on pressing for an early decision. These were anxious days. We knew that each day's delay for the sale of raisins to the United Kingdom meant some loss to some grower. There was nothing we could do but hope and pray and wait. At last, at long last, the cable which we were so hopefully and anxiously waiting for arrived on September 25th. Here is the cable: "We now in position to discuss possible purchase California seedless raisins and would welcome visit of authorized representative RAC prepared if prices and terms can be arranged, to conclude contract. Second, if RAC agree, send representative, we suggest date not earlier than 6th October. Third, it is desired that no publicity be given either to visit or suggestion of purchase.

Signed: Food Keeper."

When we met on September 29th, I wanted so much to tell you about the cable. When I spoke to the growers on September 30, I wanted so much to tell them about the great possibility of effecting the British sale. I couldn't do so because of the Ministry's desire that no publicity be given for the prospective visit or suggestion of the possible purchase.

The Operations Subcommittee met on September 29th. They reviewed the cable. They directed me to go to London at once

24

and do everything humanly possible to conclude the sale of the largest possible surplus tonnage in the quickest possible time.

I left California on October 1ˢᵗ. I met the Washington officials on October 2ⁿᵈ. They promised to help me in every way possible. They kept their promise.

I left New York on October 3ʳᵈ and arrived in London October 4ᵗʰ. On the 6ᵗʰ of October, I met with Undersecretary Phillip Keely, who had succeeded Dr. Ralph Stedman; Deputy Charles Parsons, and John Harmer, representing the Treasury.

Mr. Keely said his government had appropriated £1,710,000 Sterling, equal to $4,788,000 for the purchase of California Sultanas (they call our Thompson Seedless raisins Sultanas), and that it was his job to stretch this amount as far as it would go and use it to purchase the largest possible tonnage.

Mr. Keely said that the Ministry knew that the 1952 crop was very large and that they expected to purchase at a very attractive price. Selfish interests had advised the Ministry that if they delayed the purchase for awhile and bought bit by bit, that they would be able to purchase basis $100 to $120 per ton f.a.s.

I told Mr. Keely that I had come to London under definite instructions and would like to have a day or two to contact Washington and my people in Fresno to find out their views and advise him accordingly. Mr. Keely agreed.

I sent the following cable to Mr. Graham in Washington under date of October 6ᵗʰ: "Some packers, exporters, importers have advised the Ministry that they will be able to sell 1952 raisins basis $100 to $120 f.a.s., provided purchase can be deferred until 1953. Have told Ministry United Kingdom officially designated non-competitive country, therefore, RAC only body authorized to sell surplus raisins to United Kingdom. Recommend negotiate and if possible conclude sale following basis: 35,000 tons basis $140; 50,000 tons basis $130, or 60,000 tons basis $127.50 short tons f.a.s. Realize these prices considerably lower than prices we discussed last Thursday in Washington yet strongly urge that recommended prices be approved because: First, sale of 35,000 to 60,000 short tons will help very much wipe out uncertainty clouding 1952 raisin disposition; second, know you agree with me that we should do all humanly possible assist United Kingdom in their valiant fight to pull through. Please advise.

Signed: Setrakian.”

TERMS ARE LOWEST ACCEPTABLE

We received the following cable from Mr. Graham under date of October 7th: “RAC only agency make sale United States raisins to United Kingdom. USDA desires be helpful to United Kingdom and RAC in supplying United Kingdom raisins. Account effect of commercial sales in Europe, 35,000 tons at $140; 50,000 at $130; 60,000 at $127.50 lowest acceptable prices. Signed: Graham.”

We met with Ministry officials again on October 8th. Mr. Keely had been provided with copies of my cable to Mr. Graham and his answer. The Ministry knew that as far as we were concerned the price matter was a settled issue. The Ministry knew that it was up to them to choose which one of the three offers they thought would serve their interests best. Mr. Keely said: “We will work hard to make additional funds available so that we can take advantage of your generous gesture and purchase either 50,000 or 60,000 short tons.”

On Friday we were advised that the possibility for a decision prior to the first part of the following week looked remote.

GOES TO GENEVA

Wednesday the 8th, I flew to Geneva, Switzerland to discuss the German situation with Krikor Elmassian.

Sunday, the 12th, I got word from London that all the ob-

stacles had been surmounted and that Mr. Keely was authorized to close the purchase.

I flew to London, met the Ministry officials Monday at 2 p.m. and executed the simple and graciously worded document covering the sale of 50,000 short tons of 1952 crop surplus raisins at $130 per ton f.a.s. Here is the document:

"Dear Mr. Setrakian:

I confirm the agreement reached today concerning the purchase from the Federal Raisin Administrative Committee of 50,000 short tons of Thompson's Natural Seedless raisins of the 1952 crop at a price of $130 per short ton f.a.s.

This purchase is subject to approval of the United States Government's current subsidy on Thompson's Natural Seedless raisins, namely $50 per short ton. A contract will be drafted containing the details necessary for the proper and timely delivery of the tonnage of raisins purchased and signed by both parties as soon thereafter as possible. It is agreed that payment will be direct by the United Kingdom Treasury and Supply Delegation, Washington, D.C., against presentation of the usual document.

Please accept my thanks and that of my colleagues for the understanding which you displayed when we explained the problems which confronted us, and for the consideration which enabled us to reach agreement in such a comparatively short time, taking into account the magnitude of the contract.

We feel that the agreement reached will be a source of great benefit both to the growers of raisins in California and to the consumers in Great Britain.

Would you be good enough to sign the extra copy of this letter and return to me as a record of our agreement.

Sincerely, E. P. Keely"

I immediately contacted Mr. Hines and Mr. Jackson and told them that the deal was closed.

I cabled my statement to the Fresno Bee. We are grateful to KMJ, KFRE, KYNO, and KARM, in fact, all of the valley radio stations and press for the excellent job they did in publicizing the sale. I am especially thankful to the Fresno Bee which published my statement in full.

Soon after the deal was made, Major Lloyd George, Minister of Food, announced on the floor of Parliament: "There will be more dried fruit than for several years."

The London times had this to say: "The Ministry announced that it has made a contract with the United States for 50,000 short tons of California Sultanas of which the first shipments will arrive in the New Year."

MEETS GERMAN IMPORTERS

Mr. Krikor Elmassian and I discussed the German situation again and agreed that the most practicable way to consider the possibilities of a German sale was to meet with the outstanding importers in Hamburg, Germany and consider the whole matter collectively. We met Tuesday, October 21ˢᵗ at 2 p.m. in the office of Mr. R. Bonness, the head of Edeka, one of the largest cooperative associations in Western Germany.

Those present were Peter Elmassian, Karl Tchillingherian, Krikor Elmassian, Ernest Rickersten, George Rickersten, Leon Pisani, Wilhelm Rickersten. R. Bonness presided.

I was told that the importers attending the conference handled in excess of 50 percent of all the raisins consumed in Western Germany.

First let me repeat in the briefest way possible what I said to the German importers: "Gentlemen, I wish to thank Mr. Krikor Elmassian who has made it possible for me to meet with you. I am grateful that you have given me the privilege to meet with you. I am not here soliciting business. I am here on a good will mission.

I am here to provide you with true facts relating to the operation of the Federal Raisin Marketing Agreement and Order; the disposition of each year's crop through free, reserve and surplus pools; the approximate size of the 1952 raisin crop; the price which at present controls the sale of raisins for free tonnage use; the price under which surplus raisins may be obtained, and, most important of all, to clarify the atmosphere of the untrue statements which have been made by a few selfish persons regarding the disposition of the 1952 raisin crop.

Gentlemen, regardless of what anyone has said or may say, the only two countries which are noncompetitive and eligible to buy surplus raisins from RAC are the United Kingdom and Western Germany. We are resolved to keep the German market for our raisins in as healthy a condition as possible.

During the years of 1947, 1948, 1949, and 1951, Western Germany has used a substantial tonnage of California raisins. We are told that the German housewife likes our raisins. We know the marvelous progress you are making for economic recovery and rehabilitation.

Now that the bitter and tragic days of war are behind us, we do want to help the German people, and if given the opportunity, will provide the German consumers with California raisins at a price comparable to the price which governed the recent sale to the United Kingdom.

From all appearances, the total tonnage of Thompson Seedless raisins in the surplus pool will be approximately 62,500 short tons. Of course, this tonnage may increase if the United States market conditions make it necessary to divert raisins from the reserve pool into the surplus pool.

May I outline to you what I believe the RAC will be able to do for you in the event you should choose to purchase some surplus raisins. I want it to be definitely understood that I am not making any commitments and moreover, the final approval of any sale of surplus Natural Thompson Seedless raisins rests with the RAC.

First - if you should decide to purchase a substantial tonnage of 1952 surplus raisins, for example, 10 or 15,000 tons, we will agree to sell them to you at the price of $140 per ton f.a.s. This was the price which the United Kingdom would have paid if their purchase had been 35,000 short tons or less.

Second - we will be agreeable to give you four or possibly five months to effect shipments provided, however, that the entire amount be taken not later than June 1, 1953.

Third - RAC will agree not to sell to anyone in Western Germany during the 1952-53 raisin year any raisins at prices lower than the price governing the sale to you."

One of the importers asked the following question: "Will RAC guarantee that the price controlling the sale of raisins from the free pool will not go lower than the price which you say we will pay for surplus raisins?"

I answered: "RAC will not give any such guarantee. However, I must say that unless some exporter or packer desires to engage in the sport of losing money, such a condition cannot happen. Here are the facts: The amount of raisins allocated for free tonnage use, while ample, is not excessive for the use of markets in the United States and Canada.

If market conditions made it necessary for the packers to purchase from the reserve pool, under the law, the minimum price *controlling the sale of reserve raisins must be comparable to the average price paid by the packers for raisins bought in the field, plus the handling costs which are approximately $10 per ton. There is no chance of free tonnage raisins selling below the price of surplus raisins."*

Another importer said: "Will the raisin program continue year to year or be abolished?"

I answered: "I regret I cannot answer that question with complete accuracy. I can, however, say this to you. Raisin growers will always have something to say about the disposition of their raisins and will neither tolerate nor permit any person or group of persons to mess up the disappearance of their crop of raisins and cause unwarranted and chaotic marketing conditions.

While we are on that subject, I know you men will agree with me that any person who says things simply to confuse the minds of the buyers abroad and frighten the growers at home for greed and selfishness is doing something which is incredible, scandalous and immoral."

The conference lasted two hours and ended in an atmosphere of sympathetic understanding and friendliness.

The following day, while I was discussing the possible German purchase with Mr. Elmassian, he received the following message from New York: "No worthwhile quantities of Naturals have been sold to Germany. But the representatives of the raisin pool who have been in England are now in Germany. Tomorrow, Thursday, there will be a meeting of the Dried Fruit Association in San Francisco in order to protest government to government business.

Before Friday, I will not know whether Naturals are handled by private exporters but I conclude from Packer X's purchases that he supposes that business will be kept in private hands."

I could not believe my eyes. I could not understand what it was all about.

As late as August 21ˢᵗ, the RAC had met to consider the countries which would be declared noncompetitive for the 1952-53 raisin year. The Committee had wisely decided not to act on Sweden. The United Kingdom and Germany were declared noncompetitive.

PROTEST IS PUZZLING

Packers who voted favorably were Walter K. Hines, Ara Shapazian, Ed Foley, and Danny Hoak, and all of the grower members. I could not understand what the protest was about. But there it was.

I contacted Washington and asked for clarification, and received the following cable under date of October 24ᵗʰ: "Raisin Marketing Agreement and Order provides Committee may dispose of surplus raisins by sale, gift, or otherwise, provided such disposition limited outlets which will not interfere with normal marketing raisins or raisin variety grapes. Committee has made such findings respect exports Germany and United Kingdom. During past seven years, raisin exports commercial trade channels Germany averaged slightly less than 500 tons. As of October 22ⁿᵈ, exporters applied approval export only 1,775 tons Golden Bleached raisins Germany and 45 tons Natural Thompson raisins Germany, Holland or Belgium. Marketing Agreement and Order does not require Secretary's approval Committee's findings but Secretary has right disapproval where facts justify. USDA has no evidence which warrants disapproval Committee's findings or disapproving sale surplus Natural Thompson raisins Germany or United Kingdom.

Signed: Graham."

The cable speaks for itself. Germany is noncompetitive

until such time as the Secretary of Agriculture, for good and valid reasons, deems it proper to disapprove the RAC's decision. Such reasons do not exist now. The German situation has caused much turmoil. It has been extensively discussed by exporters and packers.

Some packers have complained to Washington and have condemned the RAC for declaring Western Germany as a noncompetitive country and my visit to Germany.

The German and Elmassian purchases of 1951 surplus raisins have been subjected to the most unjust, unfair and untrue criticism.

My first thought was to keep silent with the hope that the whole thing would die out. But because of fear that continued silence may do more harm than good to the economy of the raisin industry, I hope you will agree with me that it was wise to present the German case in detail and let the chips fall where they may.

Last May, conditions were somewhat discouraging. The domestic market was jittery and sluggish. The surplus burden appeared heavy and painful.

As stated before, I was directed to go to Europe to pave the road toward exporting large tonnages of 1952 surplus raisins. While in London, to be specific, on June 3rd, I received the following cable from the USDA: "Tyson believes Germany take some raisins. Contact Prentice, Mutual Security Agency, Bonn, for name of interested importer."

I went to Bonn. I met Mr. Hank Prentice. I learned that the chances for the sale of some three to five thousand tons of raisins to Western Germany appeared extremely favorable.

Immediately after my arrival in London, I contacted Mr. Hines and told him about the possibility of selling some raisins to Germany and suggested that RAC meet to consider the German situation.

Mr. Prentice had told me to be sure to get in touch with Peter Elmassian in London and have him arrange a meeting with his brother, Krikor, of Geneva. Mr. Prentice thought that Krikor might be interested in the purchase of some surplus raisins. I met Krikor in London. We discussed the purchase of 3,000 tons of surplus raisins with the definite understanding that the final approval rested with the RAC and the USDA.

I met USDA officials on June 14th. We completed the sale of 3,333 tons to Germany basis $150 per ton f.a.s.

I discussed with Washington the possible sale to Elmassian. I was told that Germany was noncompetitive and RAC was authorized to sell surplus raisins to any German importer, provided the raisins were used in noncompetitive eligible countries. Elmassian purchased 3,000 short tons. He pleaded for lower prices. We stood firm and Elmassian purchased 3,000 tons basis $150 per ton f.a.s.

Mr. Allmendinger knew every step taken to effect the Elmassian sale. I am at a loss to understand what we have done, what sin we have committed to cause these packers, especially one, to complain vehemently to Washington and to carry on condemning the Elmassian sales and insisting that Germany should never have been declared noncompetitive.

Indeed, facts do not support the unreasonable and unfortunate stand taken by these few packers. Here are the facts: The packers up to June 1st, 1952, had not sold one pound of Natural Thompson raisins to Western Germany. The gentleman who yells the loudest and complains the most was in London while we were trying to sell some raisins to Germany.

There was no secret about it. Everyone knew that I had gone *to Bonn. Why didn't he effect some sale from the free tonnage to the German importers? He knew that our Government had appropriated $1,000,000 for barter deals for the purchase of dried and fresh fruit.*

I am told no packer in California has closer contact and better knowledge of the export business and all the ramifications connected with barter deals than this packer. Why didn't he interest some of his contacts in Western Germany in purchasing Natural Thompson raisins from the surplus pool? Why?

What else could we have done except sell the surplus raisins when we had the chance? Western Germany and Elmassian purchased approximately 6,500 tons of raisins. The price was good. Our Government had approved the sale. The packers who have registered so many complaints and condemned the Elmassian deals so unjustly had the same chance of effecting some sales through their importers. Why didn't they do it?

The only time when we came near to making a sale was when a certain packer offered to sell to a German exporter 500 tons of surplus raisins basis $150 per ton f.a.s.

We were happy to sell his importer 500 tons.

The deal fell through because this certain packer wanted to do all the packing. The management advised the gentleman and properly so that we could not agree because the Order provides that all the packers should share equally in the packing of the surplus.

I believe it is only fair and proper that I say a word or two about the Elmassians. Prior to Mr. Prentice mentioning their names, praising them highly, I did not know that they ever existed. Our dealings with the Elmassians have proved very helpful and satisfactory. Some packers say Germany should be declared competitive. They say RAC should not sell any surplus raisins to Germany. They say they can sell Germany 10 to 15,000 tons of raisins from the free tonnage pool. They say Germans have all the dollars they need, and that they can buy our raisins from the free pool without difficulty.

True. Germany is making amazing progress for recovery and rehabilitation. True, the German stores are bulging with goods but the average income of the German people, I am told, has not kept pace with the terrific advance of the cost of living.

One German importer after another told me that unless our price for Natural Thompsons was very attractive, notwithstanding that our raisins were well received and well accepted, they would not be able to purchase any appreciable quantities.

Applications filed with the USDA for approval of contracts for the sale of Natural Thompson Seedless raisins to Germany substantiate this statement 100 percent. Here are the figures supplied by the USDA office in San Francisco showing the tonnages of Golden Bleached and sun dried Natural Thompson Seedless raisins approved for export to and including November 12th: Golden Bleached - 8,905 tons. Natural Thompson Seedless - 10,164 tons. Of this tonnage, applications approved for export to Germany amounted to: Golden Bleached - 3,004 tons. Natural Thompson Seedless - 214 tons.

In addition, an application for the export of 45 tons to either Germany, Holland or Belgium has been approved.

When we consider that all other competitive countries in European areas up to November 12th had purchased 9,950 tons, and Germany, who next to the United Kingdom consumes the largest tonnage of raisins in Europe, has purchased only 214 tons, then apparently, the hope of selling substantial quantities of raisins to Germany becomes very dim.

Germany is one of the most promising potential markets for our raisins. The importers whom I had the good fortune to meet seemed to be honorable and decent persons. The German people like our raisins. We should not pile any difficulties on the highway leading to a healthy flow of our raisins to Western Germany.

RAISINS MUST MOVE

The packers say they can sell substantial tonnages from the free tonnage. All that we want is to move raisins, maintain orderly distribution, and get the best possible returns for the growers. If the packers can sell substantial tonnages of raisins from the free tonnage, naturally, we are for it because the raisin grower will realize better returns. That is what we want.

It is our duty, that is to say, the duty of growers and packers serving on the Federal Raisin Advisory Board and the Raisin Administrative Committee to see to it that we do not suffer the surplus hardships and pains which we suffered last year.

Again, I repeat, if the packers are certain that they can sell substantial quantities of Natural Thompson Seedless raisins to Germany from the free tonnage pool, we should do everything to help them do so.

On the other hand, if economic conditions in Germany will make it impossible for the packers to sell substantial quantities of raisins from the free tonnage, then they should help us to sell to Germany from the surplus pool.

We have a common problem and the sensible and favorable solution of the problem depends upon collective effort and mutual cooperation. The question of declaring Western Germany competitive or noncompetitive is not so important as the question of what can we do in order to keep a healthy flow of our Natural Thompson Seedless raisins into Western Germany, and do everything humanly possible to not let the German people get out of the habit of eating our raisins which they like so well now.

Gentlemen, what has happened to us?

In May and June, it was my good fortune to meet and discuss with the heads of the two major packing companies our industry problems.

My hopes were lifted for a peaceful, happy and prosperous operation in the 1952-53 raisin year. Then something happened, and the raisin house became divided. We began to suffer from lack of faith in each other. And no one has been able to explain the reason why.

We cannot blame any packer who tries to protect his economy. What we are unable to understand is this:

We have a good industry. We can all make a good living out of it if we work together and have a little regard for each other's economic welfare. Take this year. We have a large crop, but because of the British sale and other prospective sales, the disposition of this year's crop does not present much difficulty. We have the tools to deal with orderly distribution effectively.

The tragedy is what we could do in an easy and pleasant way, we have to do the hard way.

Make no mistake, my friends.

EXPORTS NEED 75,000 TONS

The export outlet, year in and year out, will be able to consume not less than 75,000 tons.

The export outlet must be used to stabilize our industry and especially our domestic markets and not be used in order to demoralize the field prices and cause domestic instability and make growers and packers suffer unwarranted economic hardships.

I wished so much you were present when we were discussing the price situation with the Ministry officials. They walked with us, hand in hand on the road of equity and fair play, and with hearts full of sympathy for the growers' interests. They knew we wanted this sale badly, very badly.

And notwithstanding that some selfish interests had disregarded the livelihood of thousands of growers and their innocent dependents and tried to mislead the Ministry by advising that if they delayed buying a little, and bought little by little, they would be able to purchase raisins at ruinously low prices, yet the Ministry, knowing the proposition offered by the RAC was fair and reasonable, paid no attention. They bought and saved the day.

May I repeat from my statement which appeared in the Fresno Bee immediately after the sale was consummated: "We are going through strange times. The British people, living thousands of miles away and waging the struggle of life and death for economic survival, disregard any plan which might harm the growers' economic welfare and extend to us the helping hand and do the right thing.

Yet we have in California persons who know what the grower goes through in order to make a crop; who know how costs of production and harvesting advance daily; who know how with the passing of each day how much more raisin growers have to pay for the things they need, but still manipulate and scheme and devise ways and means through which they can demoralize the field prices, frighten the growers and force them to sell their sweat and toil, their whole year's work, their livelihood at unnecessary and unwarranted bankruptcy prices. This kind of an approach may be legal but it most certainly is morally wrong."

Our surplus problem is almost behind us. All indications are that we will not be plagued with too many raisins.

Why not advance the price to the trade to a level where packers can make a comfortable profit and pay the growers a living price for their raisins?

There is absolutely no justifiable economic reason that the growers should not receive a better field price for their free tonnage raisins. If the austerity weary British housewife can pay 18 cents per pound for raisins, is there one earthly reason that raisins in our country, rolling in wealth, should not sell at comparable prices and higher? The domestic demand is good. The export demand is good.

Short selling and speculating on the growers' sweat and toil is an ugly and nefarious practice. Those who believe that through constant agitation, aggravation and turmoil they can succeed in destroying the Raisin Order, will find out that their misspent efforts will meet with miserable defeat.

The growers are entitled to make a living out of the production of raisins and they are not going to permit anyone to kick their economy from pillar to post. There is still time to make the 1952-53 raisin year a good year if we possess the spiritual courage to work together and extend to each other the spirit of sympathetic understanding and genuine cooperation.

On October 24th, I attended the Ministry luncheon in honor of the raisin sale. Undersecretaries present were Frank Hollins, Ralph E. Stedman, and Phillip Keely; Treasury Representatives Harmer, Almond and others. The luncheon was another milepost in the continuing friendly and mutually helpful relationship between the Ministry of Food and the Federal Raisin Advisory Board. We toasted the continued prosperity of the raisin growers and packers.

The luncheon ended in an atmosphere of warm friendship and congeniality.

MAY BUY 10,000 MORE

On October 30th, we met again with Undersecretary Keely to discuss the possible purchase of an additional 10,000 tons of raisins. Here is the letter which was executed by Mr. Keely and

Seated: E. P. Keeley, C.B.E.; Sir Henry D. Hancock, K.C.B., K.B.E., C.M.G.; A. Setrakian; E. G. Harwood, C.B.; F. Hollins.
Standing: W. Kling; P. G. White, C.B.E.; R. E. Stedman; E.C.U. Wilson; Dr. Burton Baker; F. C. Parsons; Dr. W. M. Clyde, C.M.G.

NOVEMBER 1953

VOLUME 5   NUMBER 2

Published by the Raisin Administrative Committee

The voice of the RAC, *The Raisin Industry News*, published news of the RAC's international raisin transactions, including the luncheon hosted in England by A. "Sox" Setrakian to celebrate a large sale of raisins in late 1953.

your Chairman:

"Dear Mr. Setrakian:

Now that our negotiations have been so happily concluded, I should like to thank you and your associates for your very real understanding of our difficulties and above all for selling us 50,000 tons of raisins. Believe me, they will be very welcome in this country.

In a photo that first appeared in *The Raisin Industry News* in 1953 are, from left to right, William Brenner, representative of the J.M. Lowden Company; W. Lee Jackson, manager of the federal raisin program; A. "Sox" Setrakian, chairman of the board and the committee; Walter G. Rice of Reedley, vice chairman of the Federal Raisin Advisory Board; and Walter K. Hines, vice chairman of the Raisin Administrative Committee, watching as surplus pool raisins are loaded for international shipment.

I have told you there is a possibility that we may be in the market for say another 10,000 tons of raisins, and you have said that if the final harvest of the 1952 crop enables you to do so, you will give us an option on a further 10,000 tons of raisins at the price and on the terms of our present contract with you.

You have also said that you will hold this option open until 1ˢᵗ March, 1953, but, of course, if you have an opportunity of selling the raisins before that time it will be entirely agreeable for you to do so, but we would like to have you give us the opportunity to purchase the tonnage involved at the price which you have been offered by some other source, and give us ten days to exercise the option. Signed: E. P. Keely."

The same day I left for home, I met Washington officials November 3rd. They were satisfied with the sale.

The USDA officials and your Chairman met with the Ministry of Food officials at 2 p.m. on November 4th to consider the formal contract covering the British sale. The contract is similar to the contract covering the 1951 crop surplus sale, excepting two minor changes. The two changes will prove to our mutual advantage.

The first change relates to the method of payment. Last year, the United Kingdom established an irrevocable letter of credit covering the entire payment. This year, the United Kingdom on the first day of each month will deposit to the account of the RAC the funds necessary for the payment of that respective month's shipments. RAC will forward the documents as each shipment is effected to the proper British authorities in Washington.

The second change: Last year's contract provided that RAC sell raisins f.a.s. Port of Stockton or San Francisco Bay ports. This year the sales are made basis Port of Stockton, California, only. The elimination of all other ports will prove more practicable and economical.

CONTRACT IS SIGNED

Tuesday morning, November 4, Mr. G. W. Baldock, representing Her Majesty's Government and the United Kingdom Treasury and Supply Delegation and your Chairman, representing the Raisin Administrative Committee, signed the contract covering the sale of the 50,000 short tons of the 1952 crop surplus raisins. The same day I signed the application to export under the subsidy program. Mr. E. M. Graham approved the application.

The job was done.

The potential demand for our raisins in the United Kingdom and other countries in friendly areas of Europe, coupled with the Raisin Marketing Agreement and Order, makes it possible to deal with each year's crop, effectively and helpfully, regardless of its size. But this can happen only if we work together and take genuine and unselfish interest in each other's economic welfare.

Now, my friends, I want to thank you from the bottom of my heart those who sent me the kind messages while in London.

I want to repeat again anyone else would have been able to sell the same quantity under the same terms and conditions.

The United Kingdom buys our raisins because there is a definite need for our raisins. I am profoundly happy to tell you that the friendly relationship between the Ministry of Food and the RAC is at the highest level.

We are grateful to the officials of the Ministry of Food for the spirit of understanding and helpfulness which they manifested so generously.

We are grateful to the USDA which helped us in every way possible to conclude the United Kingdom sale in a relatively short time and in happy surroundings.

I am thankful and grateful that you gave me the opportunity to serve and I close with the words of Abraham Lincoln: **"Let us confidently hope that all will yet be well."**

Ultimately, through the Chairman's tireless efforts, long and demanding travel and support of the Committee and USDA representatives, 149,209 tons of reserve pool raisins were sold and shipped to the United Kingdom and 13,384 tons to West Germany during the years 1950-1954.

The young, inexperienced Federal Raisin Marketing Order soon experienced the "realities of life" and, during its first decade, faced five major and several minor challenges. Three of these challenges were resolved and the other two continue even as this treatise on the raisin industry is being written. They are reported herein, not in considered sequence of importance or even in chronological order.

CHALLENGE #1 Who should sell reserve raisins? Some raisin packers, as early as 1951, contended that the Committee should not be in the business of selling raisins in export markets. None of them came forward with a proposal for consideration by the Committee and the USDA, but they did continue their claim they should be the sellers of raisins.

When the Committee considered selling reserve raisins to West Germany in 1952, a packer claimed they were already selling to West Germany and the Committee should not compete with them. The Chairman reported to the Committee that his investigation revealed that up to June 1, 1952, that the packers "had not sold one pound of Natural Thompson raisins to West Germany." One packer came to the Committee with a request for exclusive right to sell 500 tons to West Germany. They had no sales, but requested exclusive right to sell to this market. The Committee responded they would consider any offer, but could not give exclusive rights to any single packer and no packer offers were forthcoming.

In January, 1954, the Chairman reported "the campaign to have packers sell raisins in export has started again." This campaign was spearheaded by the Dried Fruit Export Association.

Letters were sent to and personal contacts made with, representatives of the USDA. Department representatives responded they were not going to be judge and jury for settling industry differences. However, the time had arrived for the Committee to face this issue and come to a clear cut understanding as to how and by whom raisins for export should be sold.

In April of 1954, the Committee approved a Subcommittee recommendation that the sale of raisins in export be turned over to the packers and exporters. The Committee subsequently developed a system of offers whereby packers were offered raisins for export at sweatbox prices, to which packers added their costs of processing and sold such raisins to designated export markets. Export documentation was required to be sent to the Committee substantiating that such raisins were in fact exported.

In approving this program, the Committee stated that packers and exporters were on notice that the Committee reserved the right to again sell raisins in export if they failed to produce results. Results must have been satisfactory as only one limited direct export sale has been made by the Committee since 1954.

CHALLENGE #2   Raisin Quality. Very early in its existence, the Committee received reports from producers that some packers were discounting their offer prices for growers raisins, due to poor quality. In many instances, the definition of "poor quality" was not very clear. Some of the raisins exported by the Committee were also reported to be of lesser quality than others.

As is pretty typical in organizations established by commodity groups, a Subcommittee was appointed to research the issue and report their findings, and if advisable, make recommendations for solutions. Thus the issue of raisin quality and determination of conformance with such quality was assigned to an industry Subcommittee.

A whole book, or at minimum an entire chapter, could readily be written on what constitutes quality of raisins, how raisins are inspected to determine quality, and what producers can do to assure their raisins meet such minimum grade and condition standards. For purposes of this book, it is hopefully sufficient to report that after considerable discussion, recommendations for minimum grade and condition standards for both unprocessed (natural condition) and processed (packed) raisins were made.

As is required by the Federal regulations, a public hearing was held in April, 1955, at which the proposed minimum grade and condition standards were discussed. These proposals were ultimately presented to raisin producers, and through referendum procedures, approved and announced by the USDA. The proposals included a recommendation that the USDA Processed Products and Inspection Branch be the agency to inspect raisins and determine their compliance with the established minimum grade and condition standards. Subsequent to the implementation of the minimum standards, an agreement was entered into between the Committee and the Inspection Service for inspection services which have continued. The minimum grade and condition standards have been periodically reviewed and updated to meet the continuing demand for assurance of safe and healthy food.

CHALLENGE #3 International Relations. During his last sales trip to London, the Chairman was advised that Australia was a member of the "Commonwealth" and a producer of dried vine fruit which they call "Sultanas." As a member of the "Commonwealth," Australia was granted preferential privileges. Representatives from Australia had approached "Her Majesty's Government" and submitted a protest against the purchases of subsidized raisins from the United States. They contended that the purchases of U.S. raisins were having a direct impact on both the volume and price of Australian Sultanas being sold to the United Kingdom.

During a visit to London in November of 1955, the Chairman and the CEO of Sun Maid (Walter Hines) were advised that the Australians "were very restive and apprehensive" that the U.K. may become a "dumping ground" for U.S. raisins to the detriment of the Australian Sultana growers. Suggestions were made that perhaps a visit to Australia would be helpful in resolving this issue. Since reports had been made that Her Majesty's Government may have to consider implementation of restrictions or increased import tariffs on U.S. raisins, the Committee approved a delegation traveling to Australia to meet with representatives of their Sultana Industry. This delegation visit was made in May, 1956.

The U.S. Delegation was welcomed and enjoyed very friendly discussions by the Australian Dried Fruits Board Chairman, Peter Mallock, and members of the board. Within a year or two, Peter Mallock was replaced by Eugene Gorman as Chairman. Chairman Gorman, who was subsequently knighted by the Queen, had retired as a leading barrister in Australia, and devoted the rest of his life to the dried vine fruit industry of Australia and the world. Chairman Gorman and Chairman Setrakian became the closest of friends for the rest of their lives. More will be reported on this in the chapter titled "International Relations."

CHALLENGE #4 Grape Production and Crop Allocation. Thompson Seedless, from which over ninety-five percent of all raisins are produced, is a major variety for fresh table grape use and is also a multiple use grape for crushing. Its crush use has changed during the period covered by this book from wine fortification and brandy production to grape juice concentrate.

The young Federal Marketing Order was soon to experience

the impact, not only of Mother Nature, but also the decisions of grape growers in the disposition of their grape crop. Production of grapes for fresh table use requires grape growers to make major decisions at pruning time and significant changes in their cultural practices during the grape growing season. However, the decision to sell their grapes for crushing or dry them into raisins can be made in some cases almost as late as the day the grapes are harvested.

Grapes harvested for table fresh use, move almost immediately "from the field to the market." Some limited volume can be held in expensive cold storage for three or four months. Grapes crushed for alcohol or brandy production are directly impacted by the volume of other varieties of grapes available, the inventory of grape alcohol and brandy, and the price being offered by vintners. Although grapes can be stored for considerable periods of time in the form of wine and brandy, the process of converting them to wine and brandy is expensive and subsequent crops of grapes are soon available. Raisins offer the cheapest means of storage of grapes and although there is some additional cost in converting grapes into raisins, this outlet generally functions as the "surge tank" for Thompson Seedless grapes.

After struggling through two crop years of excess raisin production in 1947-48 and 1948-49, and the first year after the Marketing Order was implemented in 1949-50, a very short crop was produced in 1950-51. Industry leaders recognized that grape producers had the right of choice as to the disposition of their grapes; however, on every available opportunity they encouraged grape growers to produce sufficient raisins to maintain all their hard earned markets.

The challenge for economic stability in the raisin industry was immediate as raisin production during four crop years during the decade of the 1950's was below the market demand. The value of this new marketing order program was soon evident as carried over "surplus" was available to supply the reduced production. Although inadequate to totally fill the reduced production void, such carried over raisins did temper the violent price fluctuations and make available raisins to markets which would have had to seek their supplies from other sources.

CHALLENGE #5 Pricing. Throughout history farmers have essentially been at the mercy of commodity buyers as far as the price was concerned for which they could sell what they produced. Early in American history, this factor, perhaps more than any other, fueled the Scandinavian philosophy of farm cooperatives. Previously in this chapter, we discussed the establishment of minimum grade and condition standards and "third party inspection" for the very reason that some buyers were "downgrading" some growers raisins to purchase them at lower prices.

Some raisin buyers espoused the argument that the prices for raisins should be reduced because wineries were paying less for raisin variety grapes for crushing. These same buyers plus others contended that prices at which foreign competitors were selling their dried vine fruit, were too low for them to sell California raisins. Finally the eternal argument that other packers were selling so cheap that they could not pay higher prices to growers to compete with these unacceptable prices.

The raisin industry has a major marketing cooperative (Sun Maid Growers) which in the decade of the 1950's, claimed to represent over forty percent of the industry. They were looked to as the price leaders, and other packers set their prices below the announced Sun Maid prices. Sun Maid was a large packer of raisins in consumer packages which represented roughly one half of all industry shipments. So the real price competition occurred in the bulk package market.

In virtually every report the Chairman made to the Committee, he stated growers had the right to choose the outlet into which they sold their grapes; that growers were entitled to receive the "parity price" for their raisins and that growers needed to work together to maintain and expand their markets for raisins. The Marketing Order was a tool which proved its economic value to the raisin industry.

The Marketing Order had resulted in gaining the assistance and support of USDA representatives in the Agriculture Marketing Services and the Fruit and Vegetable Division, an introduction and beginning relationship with government representatives and dried fruit importers in Germany, Scandinavia, and the United Kingdom, and the planting of seeds with the Australian Dried Fruits industry which would result in annual conferences of world dried vine fruits producers. History would record this was but the beginning, but **"Oh what a beginning!"**

THE DECADE OF THE 1960's

After ten years of operating their Marketing Orders, it was soon obvious the grape industry still had many mountains to climb, challenges to face, and problems to solve. The never ending issue of allocation of the annual grape production took new meaning and attempts to gain a foothold on its resolution continued in the 1960's.

Use of grapes for fresh market was quite static, but appeared to be experiencing some positive growth. Competition from other fresh fruits was constant and general growth of grapes for fresh use, although small, was observed as consumers increased their fresh fruit consumption.

Grape industry leaders, who lead the development of the Federal Marketing Order for raisins, had carried their message to, and gained support from, grape growers who sold their grapes for crushing, and a Grape Crush Marketing Order was made effective in 1961. This program enjoyed a very short life and was terminated in 1963. A. "Sox" Setrakian served as Chairman of the grape crush program during its short existence while also serving as Chairman of the raisin program.

The "wine segment" of the grape industry soon learned the very difficult lesson that what works for one industry may not work for another. The grape crush program had implemented, as its basic activity, the reserve pool provisions of the Marketing Agreement Act that had been accepted as a positive solution for the raisin program.

Raisins were delivered to handlers in sweatboxes or bins and could be held in those containers for as long as two years at a very reasonable cost. Experience had been that even after storage for one or two years, such raisins could be disposed of in salvage outlets such as distillation or livestock feed for a higher price than their storage cost. In the wine industry, the grapes had to be converted to wine and held in storage tanks. It was soon learned that the processing and storage costs were such that the salvage value of grapes converted to "reserve" wine was minimal and actually depressing to grape prices in subsequent crop years.

The grape crush and raisin programs in one instance actually experienced direct confrontation. The grape crush program approved a recommendation to prohibit vintners from using raisin processing residual material, off grade raisins, and rain damaged raisins to produce high proof alcohol used to fortify wine. The raisin program opposed this action and presented information substantiating the use of residual raisins, off grade raisins, and rain damaged raisins for the production of high proof alcohol. There was no question relative to the quality of the high proof produced from such raisins or residual material. It was interesting to me -- at the time I was employed in the Marketing Field Office of the USDA involved with both the grape crush and raisin programs -- to observe one grape grower who served as a representative on both programs and who voted to prohibit the use of such off grade raisins and residual material under the grape crush program, and also voted to deny such prohibition under the raisin program.

The first international meeting of representatives of dried vine producing countries was held in Paris in the fall of 1961. Many such meetings were held in the decade of the 1960's. A formal agreement was signed by representatives from Australia, Greece, and Turkey in 1963. The U.S. was not authorized to join such an agreement and since price was a subject of considerable discussion at these Conferences, a U.S. delegation was authorized to attend the Conferences only as observers. The U.S. delegation was authorized to provide and exchange statistics and discuss production, disposition, and economic trends. These international relations will be discussed in greater detail in a later chapter.

Mr. Jack Gomperts, a dried fruit broker in San Francisco and a good friend of the Chairman, made a visit to Japan and on his return suggested to the Chairman that the time was ideal to look at Japan as a market for California raisins. Early pursuit of this suggestion resulted in learning several things about doing business in Japan.

1. Japanese importers were well organized in a group known as the Japan Dried Fruits Importers Association (JDFIA). Importers representing over ninety percent of all raisins imported into Japan were members of this Association.

2. Personal contact, in Japan, was very critical to doing business in Japan.

3. Once commitments were made, Japanese importers are very loyal customers. Further detail on the JDFIA-RAC relationship will be discussed in a subsequent chapter.

The raisin industry experienced adverse weather conditions at harvest time in the late 1950's which resulted in the loss of some drying raisins. During a visit with USDA representatives in Washington, D.C., the delegation learned that there were government insurance programs for agriculture commodities. Contacts were made and an insurance program developed which growers could purchase to insure against crop loss due to harvest rain disasters. More detail will be given in the chapter on Government Relations.

The Marketing Order requires that the Committee announce its annual marketing policy not later than the first week of October. Since announced free tonnage percentages can be increased but cannot be decreased, it is quite important that an accurate crop estimate be available for the Committee's consideration in announcing its marketing policy. The Committee funded an annual crop estimate developed by the California Crop and Livestock Reporting Service.

In 1962 the Crop Reporting Service was using a grower survey and an aerial survey to develop the estimate of sun-dried raisins. The 1962 sun-dried raisin production estimate presented to the Committee in October was 148,000 tons. Based on this information, the Committee announced the 1962 crop would be 100 percent free. Packers prices offered to growers rapidly increased from $225 per ton to $275 and in some cases $285 per ton. Many growers closed their contracts at these prices while others "held out" in anticipation prices would go even higher. One major packer did not increase his offered price above $275 per ton and in fact withdrew from the market, thus most of his contracts remained open. In late October and early November, it became apparent the crop had been under estimated, all packers withdrew their offered prices, and prices soon fell back to $225 per ton allowing the major packer, who had earlier withdrawn from the market, to close a disproportionate share of his contracts at this lower price.

Chaos in the market resulted immediately. Prices offered by packers who had paid growers $275 - $285 per ton were met by prices from other packers who had paid $225 per ton. Due to this disastrous situation and the fact free tonnage percentages under the Federal Marketing Order could not be reduced, packers petitioned the California Department of Food and Agriculture for a State Stabilization Program that would require packers to withhold a percentage of the raisins they had acquired from the market. A program was quickly developed, a public hearing held, and a referendum of raisin packers conducted. Packers representing the necessary number and volume of tonnage approved the program.

The major packer who had acquired a majority of tonnage at the reduced price challenged this program, and a panel of three judges ruled the Federal law, under which the Federal Marketing Order was established, held precedence over the State law, under which the State Stabilization Program was established, and the State Program was declared null and void. Many packers were pushed to the brink of bankruptcy as a result of a crop estimate of 148,000 tons and a final crop of 168,286 tons.

Harvest time rain occurred in 1963 and packers were busy packing raisins for normal market use and reconditioning rain damaged raisins. For the next four years the production of raisins exceeded demand. Even with the market allocation (volume) controls of the Marketing Order, the offered price disparity between packers continued to generate negative market response and acceptance. The export markets were somewhat less affected due to the reserve pool price and offer system. Prices to growers were stagnant and market demand held relatively stable at about 140,000 tons in the domestic and Canadian market, and 60,000 tons in export.

As raisin production continued to exceed demand, there was a continuing need for new and expanded markets. Industry contacts with USDA representatives included discussions of opportunities to dispose of the increasing production. Again during a visit with USDA representatives, an industry delegation learned of a surplus removal program. The industry was successful in getting raisins included in this program and over the next thirty plus years, in excess of 227,700 packed tons of raisins would be sold under government feeding programs. More detail will be given in the chapter on Government Relations.

Packers maintained that the "open price contracts" with growers resulted in too great a disparity in prices at which packers acquired raisins from growers. This coupled with their contention that California raisins were over priced in the World Market and thus they could not increase raisin exports.

In 1997 I learned from John Pakchoian that during a raisin industry delegation visit to Washington, D.C. in the mid-1960's, the Chairman suggested a Raisin Bargaining Association be organized. Mr. Pakchoian was a member of the delegation and he said the tomato growers had just established a bargaining association and "Sox suggested the raisin growers organize under the cooperative laws of the State of California." Mr. Pakchoian said this issue was discussed by individuals and small groups during the subsequent months.

Ernest Bedrosian advised that he discussed the matter of a raisin growers bargaining association with several growers and grape industry representatives. The Cling Peach industry had a successful bargaining association in operation. He discussed this association with Ralph Bunje, who was looked to as the expert on grower bargaining associations.

A meeting of raisin growers was scheduled and announced to be held at Bruce's Lodge, which was on Old 99 between Fowler and Selma, in the fall of 1966. The subject of this meeting was a raisin bargaining cooperative and the objective was to determine the amount of support for such an association. Sufficient support was expressed that a committee was organized and activities started to establish a bargaining association.

At raisin delivery time in the fall of 1966, the raisin growers were trying to get packers to increase their offered prices for free tonnage Natural (sun-dried) Seedless raisins from $240 to $250 per ton. Their efforts were unsuccessful and growers even walked picket lines at some packer's plants. The organizing committee intensified their efforts. District meetings were held, personal grower to grower contacts were made, a target tonnage was set, growers were signed up, and State representatives contacted to begin the process of establishing an association.

In February of 1967, the organizers announced the target tonnage had been signed up and the Raisin Bargaining Association (RBA) began its existence. Once the announcement was made that the RBA was in operation, many additional growers signed on, increasing the tonnage represented by the Association significantly. It was quite obvious the efforts to establish a bargaining association included many growers, but Ernest Bedrosian (Ernie) was recognized as the "father" of the RBA and was elected its first president.

The production of sun-dried seedless raisins in 1967 was 161,321 tons following large crops in the previous years. A large tonnage of raisins was carried into the 1967-68 crop year, and yet the RBA negotiated a free tonnage price of $307 per ton, up from the $240 per ton for the 1966-67 crop. With the establishment of the RBA, grower open price contracts ceased to exist and a uniform free tonnage field price was implemented.

The "airstream sorter" was used on the 1967 crop in a "dry run" to determine if it was a reliable tool to determine raisin quality. With the reduced 1967 production and excellent maturity raisins, the results of this dry run were very positive and minimum maturity standards were implemented for the 1968 crop using the airstream sorter to determine the volume of substandard raisins in growers deliveries. Chaos reigned supreme at delivery time for the higher volume, lower quality 1968 crop. The manometer setting on the airstream sorter was lowered to 47, grower complaints were reduced, and the crop was delivered. The airstream sorter continues to be used to determine raisin maturity.

In the closing months of 1969, Kalem Barserian was employed as the General Manager of the Raisin Bargaining Association. Kalem had been employed by the Committee as a fieldman and was the RAC Controller at the time of his employment by the RBA. In his position as General Manager, Kalem together with Frank Light would take leadership rolls in many major changes in the Federal and State Marketing Orders during the decade of the 1970's, and well into the decade of the 1980's.

Raisin shipments into both the domestic and Canadian markets as well as the export market remained static. Dialogue began in the industry that something had to be done to market the increasing annual production of sun-dried seedless raisins. Production of sun-dried seedless raisins in the last two years of the decade, 1968 and 1969, was 240,929 and 227,429 tons, and the annual disposition was remaining fairly static at about 210,000 to 220,000 tons. The challenge was here and something needed to be done to meet it.

THE DECADE OF THE 1970's

The 1970's started with two below-normal years of sun-dried seedless raisin production. With the carryover of unsold reserve tonnage from the large 1968 and 1969 crops, the markets were supplied, but the carryover was exhausted.

The production of raisin variety grapes in 1970 and 1971 was 2,155,000 and 1,871,000 tons respectively. The crush for these varieties was 851,000 and 1,204,000 tons which resulted in Natural (sun-dried) Seedless raisin production of only 176,066 and 172,347 tons respectively.

The California Raisin Advisory Board funded a market study in 1970 conducted by Fresno State University Vice President, Dr. Charles E. Swanson. The report issued at the conclusion of this project became known as "The Swanson Study" and became the basis for much of the industry's marketing activity for the next twenty years. This study will be covered in greater detail in a subsequent chapter, but for purposes here, it concluded that increased funding for generic advertising of California raisins and use of electronic media could significantly increase the demand for California raisins. As a result of this information, the advertising assessment was increased and efforts began to promote California raisins.

During a delegation visit to Washington, D.C., Floyd F. Hedlund, Director of the Fruit and Vegetable Division, advised the delegation of a provision in the Marketing Agreement Act applicable to imports. This provision in Section 608(e) of the Act requires that imports must meet import standards comparable to those established for industries in the U.S. Mr. Hedlund commented since the raisin industry had established minimum

63

grade and condition standards for raisins produced in California, they may want to consider such standards for imports.

To provide for import standards would require Congressional amendment to specifically add raisins to Section 608(e) of the Act. Since the Committee is not permitted to directly petition Congressional representatives, the RBA contacted Congressman B. F. Sisk and made such a request. Congressman Sisk was a good friend of the raisin industry and many industry representatives. It was the industries good fortune that he was also Chairman of the House Agriculture Subcommittee. Industry representatives went to Washington to testify before this Subcommittee relative to the merits of an amendment to the Act to provide for import standards. Little did the industry know when this amendment was approved and implemented that the wrath of Mother Nature during the decade of the 1970's, resulting in significant imports of dried vine fruit, would test the value of the amendment.

The Federal Raisin Advisory Board was stunned when at the close of a meeting held on July 1, 1971, the Chairman stated, "My friends, for several months I have been seriously considering to retire from the Federal Raisin Advisory Board as soon as my term expired. However, early in 1971 disturbing reports indicated that the life of the International Sultana (Raisin) Agreement was in jeopardy. Moreover, these reports indicated that there was a slight chance of saving the Agreement, provided an American Delegation attended the June 7, 1971 London Conference. I gave up the idea of retiring and was elected as a member of the Federal Raisin Advisory Board."

"You recall that when we met last time I said, 'It is anyone's guess whether we will witness the establishment of a new Agreement or the burial of an instrument which had improved the return to Sultana and raisin producers all over the world.' Well, we know what happened to the Agreement in the June London Conference."

"There are many members serving on the Federal Raisin Advisory Board who can discharge the duties and responsibilities of Chairman as well as I can and better. Therefore, my friends, I have decided to retire from the Board as of today."

"My friends, you who serve on the Board, who take time out of your crowded responsibilities so that you can help someone who needs your help, enjoy a thrill which no amount of money can buy. I pity anyone who has not experienced the thrill of helping someone who needed his help."

"My parting appeal to you is: Keep up the good work."

"Now for a word or two about myself…. The Preacher, Son of David, King of Jerusalem, had this to say: (Ecclesiastes Chapter III, Verses I and IV), 'There is a time to weep. There is a time to laugh.' There is no need to weep. I have served on the FRAB and RAC some 22 years. Gigantic strides have been made to bring about orderly distribution, stability, and reasonably fair returns to the raisin producer. 'There is a time to laugh.' I laugh because the raisin industry is in sound, healthy condition. I laugh with a heart full of joy when I witness how growers, packers, and all related interests labor in the vineyard of harmony and friendly understanding."

"I have enjoyed working with the members of FRAB and RAC for 22 years. They have been glorious years. I part wishing all of you and your dear ones good health, good fortune, and good luck."

"God bless you all… goodbye."

The standing applause given The Chairman at the end of this, his last speech to the Board, put a giant exclamation point at the end of a brilliant leadership period in the California raisin industry.

Growers and other industry representatives arrived at a public hearing on March 28 and 29, 1972, which had been called to consider amendments to the Marketing Order, with reports of a "killer frost" which had been experienced each of those two mornings. By the end of the week, as one drove through the raisin grape area, one could observe vineyards which appeared as if they had been in a gigantic forest fire.

At the time this frost struck, the new vine growth was out from 10 - 15 inches, and the new crop grape bunches were already visible. Some growers harvested no grapes; some from 1 to 3 tons of green grapes, and many 4 to 6 tons on vineyards which in normal years would produce 8 to 12 tons of grapes.

This disastrous frost resulted in the production of raisin variety grapes of only 1,344,000 tons. However, the demand for crushing was 717,000 tons, which resulted in the production of only 91,258 tons of Natural (sun-dried) Seedless raisins. With the limited tonnage carried over from prior years prices increased and market allocation resulted. The 1972-73 crop was declared 100% free, and the Committee had no reserve tonnage with which to maintain export markets.

Free tonnage prices increased from $320 per ton in 1971 to $500 per ton in 1972 and $700 per ton in 1973. These experiences of the raisin industry graphically demonstrated two statements made by one of my college professors and never forgotten. One statement was that "prices generally go up by the escalator and farm prices by the stairwell." Certainly two large steps occurred in 1972 and 1973 but more was yet to come. The second statement was that "when farm prices drop they seldom go to the level from which they advanced." This also was the case in the raisin industry as growers prices in 1974 dropped back to $640 per ton.

Production returned to normal or more in 1973, 1974 and 1975. Marketing conditions began to stabilize again after the short 1970 and 1971 crops, and the disaster of 1972. Foreign buyers who had questioned the reliability of an adequate supply of raisins from California began to return. Then came the harvest time rains of 1976. The crop was laid out to dry and growers were virtually helpless as rain and cool weather continued. Growers knew that rain damaged raisins could be reconditioned if they could just get them dry. With the long adverse weather period, many grapes/raisins deteriorated to the point the producers just disced them in the field.

Raisin handlers and reconditioners experimented with and developed new equipment and methods to recover marketable raisins from raisins damaged during the drying process in years of adverse weather. The 1976 production of raisin variety grapes was 2,250,000 tons and the crush was 755,000 tons; however, the production of sun-dried seedless raisins was only 117,605 tons. Field prices again escalated to $1050 per ton. With the carried over reserve from the 1973 - 1975 crops, and reduced demand due to higher prices, the industry was able to meet the market demand.

In 1977 production increased to 218,813 tons and field prices fell to $840 per ton. With the horrors of the harvest of 1976 still pretty clear in growers minds, harvest time adverse weather in 1978 was even worse than that of 1976. The production of raisin variety grapes was 1,908,000 tons and the crush 702,000 tons. Inspite of all the revolutionary equipment and reconditioning methods, the industry was only able to salvage 74,410 tons of sun-dried seedless raisins (the smallest crop since 1915), and free tonnage prices increased to $1600 per ton. Questions of reliability of supply and reasonable prices were raised again by both domestic and export buyers. Some packers imported raisins from Afghanistan, Mexico, and Turkey in an effort to supply their normal buyers.

The 1979 production was 263,108 tons, indicating an increasing production trend and free tonnage prices again dropped to $1150 per ton.

The California "wine boom" began in the 1970's with one economist stating that grapes could not be planted in California and brought into production fast enough to meet the exploding demand. The bearing acreage of wine varieties of grapes increased from 131,800 acres in 1970-71 to 315,175 acres in 1977-78. Production of all varieties of grapes in California broke the 4,000,000 ton barrier in 1978-79 at 4,017,000 tons and 5,000,000 tons in 1980-81. With the increase in bearing acreage of wine grapes and increased per acre production on the new acreage, the use of raisin variety grapes for crushing began a downward trend that would not bottom out until 1994.

In addition to the resignation of Mr. Setrakian from the Board and the Committee after 22 years of serving as the Chairman and the crop disasters created by Mother Nature, several other changes were experienced which had immediate and long term impact on the raisin industry.

In 1972 Frank R. Light was employed as the President and CEO of Sun Maid Growers of California. In 1980 Sunsweet Prunes and Diamond Walnuts joined Sun Maid to form a marketing federation called Sun Diamond Growers. Frank was employed as the President and CEO of Sun Diamond as well as each of the Federation member cooperatives. Frank and Kalem Barserian gave leadership to many major changes in the Federal and State Marketing Orders well into the decade of the 1980's.

In the mid 1970's a Federal law was passed that required, among other things, that all Federal Advisory Boards must publish their meeting notices in the Federal Register at least 10 days prior to each meeting. The meeting notice must include each agenda item and no other items could be added after publication or at the Board Meeting. Since the Raisin Marketing Order had a Raisin Advisory Board and an interpretation had been made that this fell under the jurisdiction of this new law, the industry requested a public hearing in 1976 to address this and other issues.

The industry had labored under the task of determining and recommending the volume of raisins to be declared as free tonnage each year. Some packers and most growers favored this tonnage being as large as possible. Other packers and few growers favored this tonnage being tight. Previous years discussions had been so heated that the Department of Agriculture requested a 24-hour "cooling off period" between the time the Advisory Board considered this issue and made its recommendation to the Committee. The Committee was the administrative body for the Marketing Order and reviewed all recommendations from the Board before submitting their recommendations to the Department of Agriculture for approval and implementation. A system for determining and announcing the annual trade demand was included in the 1976 hearing.

Other issues were included in the 1976 hearing but these two major issues resulted in major changes in the operation of the Marketing Order. The issue of the Advisory Board was resolved by growers voting in a referendum to eliminate the sixteen (16) member Raisin Administrative Committee. The forty-seven (47) member Raisin Advisory Board was re-designated as the Committee. This change eliminated the "Advisory Board" under the Marketing Order and thus removed the requirement to comply with the Federal Advisory Board Act.

The system approved for recommending an annual free tonnage was the establishment of a statistical formula which used as its base the shipments of free tonnage raisins during the prior crop year or in instances of reduced shipments due to adverse weather, the Committee could select one of the prior three years as the base. This activity occurs before any grapes are laid to dry in a crop year, and the system does include checks and balances to meet errors in crop estimates, major changes in market conditions, etc.

Another major change in the operation of the Marketing Order resulted from the 1976 hearing, not as a result of an industry proposal, but rather from an interpretation issued by the Department of Agriculture. In the late 1950's when the sales of surplus tonnage into export markets was turned over to the packers, a system of offers was implemented. The "raw product price" for raisins sold into export is, and has historically been, less than that for raisins sold in the domestic and Canadian markets. Transportation costs, import duties, and international monetary exchange in many cases result in foreign consumers paying prices equal to or higher than domestic consumers. This system of surplus pool sales provided for the Committee making periodic offers of surplus pool raisins to packers at an announced price. These offers included an allocation of the tonnage offered, based on each packer's percentage of free tonnage acquired, a time period during which such offered tonnage could be purchased and a period of time during which the tonnage purchased must be exported. In some crop years, surplus pool offers were made every ten days to two weeks. Eight to ten offers were common to dispose of a surplus pool, and seventeen offers were made to dispose of the 1959-60 surplus pool.

By the mid 1970's packers' complaints had been registered that in many cases the amount of the offer and the export periods were too short. Longer periods were requested to allow packers and foreign buyers to better plan for long term programs to encourage increased sales. Some packers had limited export business and seldom purchased the tonnage allocated and offered to them. Other packers were very active in exporting California raisins and seldom had enough tonnage allocated and offered to them.

In announcing the results of the 1976 referendum, the Department of Agriculture issued an interpretation that the sales of all California raisins, domestic and Canada and all export markets, must be supplied from free tonnage. This caused temporary chaos in the market for California raisins, since there continued to be a significant differential in the prices at which raisins could be sold in the domestic and Canadian and export markets. This dilemma resulted in the industry quickly developing and implementing what became known as the Export Adjustment Offer Program.

The Export Adjustment Offer Program, to the raisin industry, is a relatively simple program, but to those not in the industry a fairly complicated program. Reasons for trying to understand these programs are many, but the simple bottom line is that the Committee establish a raw product price different than the free tonnage price for raisins sold in export markets. The raisin industry never seems satisfied to develop and implement simple programs, so they complicated the Export Adjustment Offers by establishing different adjusted prices for different export markets.

For those readers of this book who wish to become experts

in the Export Adjustment Offer Programs, a relatively simple formula was developed to determine the volume of reserve tonnage offered packers to adjust their export raw product prices. Using this formula, x = the free tonnage price, y = reserve price, and z = the desired adjusted price. Thus $x + y = z$. Using a free tonnage price of $1160, a reserve price of $100, and a desired raw product export price of $810, the computations are as follows:

$$\$1160x + \$100y = \$810z$$
$$1160x - 100y = 810z - 100y$$
$$1060x = 710z$$
$$x = 66.981\% \text{ and } y = 33.019\%$$
$$\$1160 \text{ X } 66.981\% = \$776.98$$
$$100 \text{ X } 33.019\% = \underline{\ 33.02}$$
$$\text{Adjusted Price } = \$810.00$$

A packer who had an export sale for 100 tons of raisins would pack and ship raisins from their free tonnage inventory. They would then provide substantiating export documentation to the Committee and apply for 33.02 tons of reserve pool raisins and submit payment of $3302.00. The Committee would release 33.02 tons of reserve to the packer which then became free tonnage and the packer can sell this tonnage at any price and in any market.

The industry gave a sigh of relief that the decade of the 1970's was behind them and looked forward to a more reasonable decade of the 1980's.

THE DECADE OF THE 1980's

The decade of the 1980's opened with great challenges to the raisin industry. The weather disasters of the 1970's had caused record low production of raisins in 1972, 1976 and 1978, which resulted in free tonnage prices going from $325 per ton in the 1971-72 crop year to $1600 per ton in the 1978-79 crop year. Free tonnage prices had fallen back to $1150 per ton in 1979-80, but were on the increase again as the decade of the 1980's began.

As a result of the increase in free tonnage raisin prices and the wine boom, vineyard prices had increased from $2500-3500 per acre in 1971-72 to $12,000-15,000 per acre as the decade of the 1980's began. The new plantings of wine variety grapes were beginning to reach full production. Due to the area in which these new plantings were being made, many on drip or other up-dated irrigation systems, this new acreage was producing double the volume of grapes per acre of "traditional" wine grapes. The demand for raisin variety grapes for crushing began to fall and the production of sun-dried seedless raisins increased, exceeding the 300,000 ton barrier in 1983-84, and only dropping below this barrier to 299,423 tons in one crop year (1984-85) during the next twelve crop years.

Greece had applied for membership in the European Common Market (subsequently changed to the EU or European Union). Prices for Sultanas had been kept high as Greece anticipated the EU would accept their support price for Greek Sultana producers. This proved correct, as the EU did accept these support prices. Due to these artificial high prices, at the time of Greece's entrance into the EU, on January 1, 1981, virtually the entire 1980-81 Greek Sultana crop remained unsold when the

1981-82 crop was harvested in August - September 1981. Export prices began to fall.

The RBA was again promoting an increase in the advertising/promotion assessment rate to hopefully increase raisin sales to meet the increasing raisin production. Sun Maid opposed this increase. Frank Light had stated Sun Maid would not support an increase in this assessment rate until a program was developed to give "brand" owners some credit for their assessment to promote their own brand of raisins. After much discussion on this issue and a "lock up" of industry leaders in the Holiday Inn in Santa Nella, a Credit Back Program was approved, a hearing and referendum conducted, and the program implemented in 1982. This program limited "credit back" to roughly 75% of the packer-only assessment, required the packer to spend two dollars on eligible advertising/promotion activity to get one dollar "credit back" and limited eligible advertising-promotion activity to a packer's own brand. No "credit back" could be earned for promotion of private brands (store brands or brands not owned by the packers).

Adverse weather was again experienced in the fall of 1982-83. The sun-dried seedless raisin production fell to 205,700 tons, was declared 100% free tonnage, and the price increased to $1300 per ton. Signs of disaster began to appear. It was obvious something had to be done. All available solutions were very unpleasant.

The 1983-84 production of sun-dried seedless raisins was a then record of 347,943 tons. Negotiated free tonnage prices remained at $1300 per ton but free tonnage percentages were at record low of 37.5 percent. The economy of the raisin industry crashed. The agriculture depression, which had been going on for two to four years in other parts of the nation, arrived in California with a devastating impact.

After much soul searching, discussion, alternative investigation and finally heart breaking reality, the raisin industry approved a free tonnage inventory adjustment program, and a free tonnage price for the 1984-85 crop of $700 per ton was negotiated. Packers were offered one ton of reserve raisins at $100 per ton for each ton of free tonnage inventory they held on July 31, 1984. This reserve tonnage was released to the packers in equal increments during the next ten months following approval of the adjustment program.

The disastrous impact of this crash resulted in some vineyard buyers simply walking away from their vineyards and letting them revert to the previous owners who were carrying the papers. Banks and other farm credit institutions ended up being owners of much vineyard acreage as buyers declared bankruptcy or simply abandoned their vineyards.

Some lenders imposed a provision in their lending contract called a "Judicial Foreclosure." This provision allowed the lender to hold the borrower liable for the shortage between what the borrower had remaining on their loan and the price the lender was able to obtain from reselling the vineyard. Many growers who had other vineyards as assets were indebted for as long as ten years before they were able to clear the financial burden imposed on them through these judicial foreclosure actions.

The RAC Chairman for the first 22 years of the existence of the Marketing Order often used quotations in his speeches and reports to the Committee. One of those quotes was, "After the rain, comes the sun." In these dark days the raisin industry was certainly looking for the sun. However, it was also accepted that the industry had to do what it could to help itself.

Mr. John D. Pakchoian was a producer of grapes, raisins, almonds, and cotton. He was a member of the RBA and the RAC.

The Federal government had developed and implemented a Payment In Kind (PIK) Program for cotton producers. John was a participant in the PIK Program and also on the Fresno County ASCS Committee which administered this Program. In discussions with Kalem Barserian, then Manager of the RBA, and other industry representatives, John suggested the raisin industry consider a Payment In Kind Program. Within a year a Raisin Diversion Program was developed -- of which John is credited as being the father -- a hearing and referendum conducted, and the Program implemented.

The Raisin Diversion Program (RDP), which appears to non-raisin industry people to be quite complicated, is a relatively simple program. Without getting into the specific detail, each year on or before November 30, the Committee reviews raisin supply and demand information and determines and announces the reserve tonnage, if any, available for a diversion program. The tonnage and details of the Program are mailed to all raisin producers of record with the Committee. This Program is totally voluntary and producers who wish to participate in the Program then submit an application to the Committee identifying the production unit (vineyard) they wish to divert and the volume of raisins produced on that unit during the current crop year. If more tonnage is applied for than the Committee has announced as available, a lottery drawing is held and sufficient applications drawn to equal the announced diversion tonnage.

When a producer's application is approved, the approved application is mailed to them. The producer must then remove the vines on the approved production unit, if the producer indicated on the application he was going to remove the vines, or he must spur prune the vines and take any other measures necessary to assure no grapes are produced and harvested for any use on that production unit. Subsequent to June 1 of that crop year, RAC Compliance Examiners physically visit each approved production unit to verify the producer has complied with the terms and conditions of the RDP. RAC Compliance Examiners drive through each vineyard on four wheeled ATV vehicles to verify the entire grape production on each unit has been properly diverted.

If compliance is verified, for the subsequent crop year the producer is issued a Diversion Certificate by the Committee equal to the weight of raisins produced on their diverted production unit during the previous crop year. The weight on this certificate is equal to the weight of the raisins from that production unit reported to the RAC by the packer who acquired those raisins from the producer. The producer then takes the certificate and markets it to a packer. The producer and packer negotiate terms of sale for free tonnage the same as if the producer were delivering raisins.

The packer deducts costs, equal to the harvest cost announced at the time the diversion tonnage was announced, from payment to the producer. The packer then submits the Diversion Certificate to the RAC with all applicable payments and the RAC releases raisins to the packer from the reserve pool equal to the weight on the Diversion Certificate.

The RDP is a tool and not a solution. A diversion program has been announced and implemented during nine crop years during the thirteen crop years 1985-86 through 1997-98. The annual tonnage diverted has varied from 2,051 tons to 103,606 tons, the total volume diverted in these nine crop years was 419,439 tons.

In 1984 Senator Jesse Helms introduced a bill into Congress which was approved and gave the Secretary of Agriculture $175 million which could be used at the discretion of the Secretary to promote U.S. agriculture commodities in export markets. These funds were essentially all used for major basic commodities; i.e., wheat, cotton, corn, soybeans, tobacco, etc. Unknown to the raisin industry, Kalem Barserian and Frank Light were working with USDA and political representatives to get access to some of these funds. As then Manager of the California Raisin Advisory Board, I received a telephone call late one October afternoon in 1984. Kalem was calling from Washington, D.C. to advise that they had successfully received commitment for some of the "Helms Funds." He stated: "Clyde, Frank and I have just gotten a commitment for $4.5 million of 'Helms Funds.' That's the good news. The bad news is that you need to get a marketing plan submitted to FAS in two weeks and the funds need to be spent in the next twelve months. We'll give you the details when we get home." More detail on the Helms Funds will be included in a subsequent chapter. In reviewing this issue, the raisin industry was the first special products commodity to be given advertising/promotion discretionary funds by the Secretary.

With the increased funds available to the industry as a result of the increased assessment rates beginning in 1971 and increased again in 1983, periodic research was conducted to obtain information on who was purchasing raisins, how often were they purchasing raisins, how were they being used, etc. In one of these research surveys, a question was asked of consumers, "How do you perceive a raisin?" Perception was a new "buzz word" in the world of advertising/promotion and the raisin industry thought it would be good to learn how they measured up. The response to this question was quite alarming. These responses included a raisin is dull, dry, uninteresting, wimpy, unattractive, with very few positive responses. As a result, the charge was given to the

CALRAB staff and the advertising/promotion agency to come up with a strategy and a program to change the consumers perception of a raisin. The detail and results of this challenge will be covered in a subsequent chapter.

By the close of the decade of the 1980's, free tonnage prices for sun-dried seedless raisins had increased from $700 per ton in 1984-85 to $1115 per ton in 1989-90. Returns to producers on 100 percent of their crop had increased from $573 in 1983-84 to $987 in 1989-90. Shipments of sun-dried seedless raisins had increased from 212,528 packed tons in 1982-83 to 338,172 packed tons in 1988-89 with a slight drop to 330,171 packed tons in 1989-90.

Below: Rows of Central Valley raisins in various stages of drying.

Above: The ubiquitous California Dancing Raisins in Washington, D.C.

Above: A Central Valley, California raisin vineyard

Below: Terracing equipment, Central Valley, California.

Right & Below: Grapes being laid down on trays to begin the drying process.

Below: Dried
raisins and
rolled trays,
Central Valley,
California.

Greek Sultana
vineyards

CRETE

GREECE

**Right and Below:
Australian Drying
Racks. (Photos
courtesy Australian
Dried Fruits Board.)**

A
U
S
T
R
A
L
I
A

Above: Australian rack spraying. (Photo courtesy Australian Dried Fruits Board.)

AUSTRALIA

Right: Australian mechanical harvester. (Photo courtesy Australian Dried Fruits Board.)

TURKEY

Above: Turkish dipping facility. (Photo courtesy Erdinç Kapkaç)

Above and Below: Turkish drying yards. (Photo courtesy Erdinç Kapkaç)

Above: Turkish drying yards. (Photos courtesy Erdinç Kapkaç)

Below: Turkish drying yards. (Photos courtesy Erdinç Kapkaç)

Above and Below: Turkish hand cleaning after processing. (Photos courtesy Erdinç Kapkaç)

Below: Turkish delivery containers. (Photos courtesy Erdinç Kapkaç)

Above: Meticulous care is taken as raisins are sorted in a Turkish processing plant. (Photo courtesy Erdinç Kapkaç)

THE DECADE OF THE 1990's

T he bright dawning of the decade of the 1990's was soon faced with potential problems. The 1980's ended with record shipments at grower prices surprisingly recovered from the disastrous levels of 1983 and 1984.

Clouds of variable size and darkness appeared on the horizon of the 1990's. The volume of raisin variety grapes purchased for crushing fell to a low of 270,000 tons in 1990-91 and to an unbelievable low of 197,000 tons in 1994-95. With the bearing acreage of raisin variety grapes remaining at virtually the same level, and the increase in use of grapes for fresh table use coming from new red seedless varieties of grapes, the annual production of Natural (sun-dried) Seedless raisins flirted with the 400,000 ton mark.

Rumblings increased in frequency and volume from the packer segment of the industry. Some packers contended the advertising/promotion credit back program was unfair and they were unable to get amendments considered to level the playing field. Thus, as detailed elsewhere in this book, in the spring of 1994 a petition, signed by fourteen packers representing a majority of all raisins processed, was delivered to the Secretary of The California Department of Food and Agriculture. Pursuant to this petition, the State Marketing Order was terminated effective July 31, 1994, and the funds generated thereunder for advertising/promotion of California raisins existed no more.

Some packers contended the reserve raisins released pursuant to the Export Replacement Program were hemorrhaging back into the free tonnage supply and creating instability in the market. Appeals were made to the Committee and amendments made to the trade demand formula which reduced the "desirable carry out" from three months to two and one-half months, two and one-quarter months and eventually two month shipments of the prior crop year.

In spite of the tightening market, instability continued. Shipments into both the domestic and export markets began to fall. Eventually a proposal was presented to and approved by the Committee to discontinue the Export Adjustment Program, and replaced it with a 100 percent Cash Adjustment Offer Program. This Program immediately spawned long and heated discussions relative to which reserve pool should provide cash for the Adjustment Program; how many months of exports should be covered by each reserve pool; and what is done when there is not enough cash in a reserve pool to cover the earned export adjustment?

Contentions were made that prices for exports were too high. We were losing export sales due to cheaper prices from competitive suppliers. The Committee was again convinced to reduce adjusted prices for exports of California raisins. Early results of these price reductions are that shipments to export markets are still falling.

During the four years following the termination of the State Marketing Order on July 31, 1994, discussions, formal and informal, occurred relative to development of a new market promotion program. In mid-1997, under the leadership of the Raisin Bargaining Association, a proposed program was drafted and meetings of raisin growers and packers were held to discuss the proposal. Compromises were made in an effort to develop a program which would be jointly funded and administered by growers and packers.

During a meeting held in December of 1997, several independent packers announced they would not accept the program, stating, "You can count me out" -- and left the meeting.

Early in 1998, under the leadership of the Raisin Bargaining Association and Sun Maid Growers, discussions began for a "grower only" program. By late spring of 1998 a proposed grower only program was submitted to the Secretary of the California Department of Food and Agriculture, and a request made for a public hearing to consider this program. Pursuant to this request a hearing was held and the Secretary determined sufficient testimony was received in support of the program to submit it to growers in a referendum.

On July 24, 1998, the California Department of Food and Agriculture issue the results of the referendum. There were 3,671 eligible growers to whom referendum information and ballots were mailed. Of these eligible growers, 2,622 (71 percent) submitted valid ballots.

Of those submitting valid ballots, 2,294 (87.49 percent), representing 81.77 percent of the total volume of raisins produced in the 1997 crop year, voted in favor of the program. There were only 328 ballots returned voting in opposition to the program.

On August 7, 1998, the first meeting of the California Raisin Marketing Board, appointed by the Secretary, was held and officers elected.

As this book goes to press, the jury is still out. It appears the "culprit" has not yet been identified and apprehended. Who knows whether the decade of the 1990's will end with a boom or a bust?

Below: The first meeting of the California Raisin Marketing Board.

Part Two

The Marketing Orders

THE RAISIN ADMINISTRATIVE COMMITTEE (RAC)

The Federal Marketing Order, with its administrative body the Raisin Administrative Committee (RAC), and the State Marketing Order, the California Raisin Advisory Board (CALRAB), were both approved through the applicable referendum process and made effective in the fall of 1949. The primary provisions of the Federal Program are volume control and minimum grade and condition standards. The primary provisions of the State Program were advertising/promotion and research. As the years passed, the functions of these Programs have been amended and expanded into areas their founders did not visualize.

Each of these Programs had separate administrative bodies, administrative staffs, and separate offices until 1976 when they moved into the same building but were separated by a storage, print, and conference room. In fact the hall door between the two offices was "bugged" with an electronic device. Since both bodies used the conference room and restrooms, this electronic device was turned off during normal business hours.

In 1977, I had been the manager of the RAC since 1968, and was asked and accepted the additional position of CALRAB manager. In 1986, the offices were moved to another building where there were no physical barriers between the staffs of the two programs. However, employees continued to be employed by either the RAC or CALRAB with management and some supervisory services provided through an agreement between RAC and CALRAB.

The founders of the Federal Marketing Order desired a broader base of grower representatives. Their hope was that this broader base would bring greater expertise to discussion of industry issues and also carry the actions of the industry back to raisin growers. Thus a Federal Raisin Advisory Board comprised of forty-five members was established. The Board size was increased to forty-six in 1967 and to forty-seven in 1976.

During the twenty-five years of the existence of the Federal Raisin Advisory Board, it had only two Chairmen. A. (Sox) Setrakian was the Chairman from 1949 until July of 1971, and Ernest A. Bedrosian from July 1971 until the Board was discontinued in August of 1976.

The administrative body of the Federal Marketing Order has always been the Raisin Administrative Committee (RAC or Committee). Initially this body was comprised of fourteen members. The Committee was increased to fifteen members in 1967. All matters were reviewed by the Committee and approved recommendations submitted to the Secretary of Agriculture for review and approval.

The Raisin Administrative Committee has had seven Chairmen and five Managers. The Chairmen are elected annually by the Committee and the Managers are hired by the Committee. During the author's twenty-seven years of service as Manager, no written employment agreement was implemented. The Chairmen serve without financial compensation for their many hours of service. They do receive reimbursement for mileage to and from meetings, and their travel expenses as industry representatives to International Conferences, foreign market visits, leaders of delegations visiting government representatives, etc. Following is a schedule of the RAC Chairmen and their term of office, and the Managers and their term of employment:

Chairman	Term of Office
A. (Sox) Setrakian	August 1949 - July 1971
Allen Mather	August 1971 - June 1973
Henry C. Klein, Jr.	June 1973 - May 1986
John D. Pakchoian	May 1986 - July 1988
Richard Garabedian	July 1988 - July 1990
Pete J. Penner	July 1990 - June 1996

Norman Engelman	June 1996
Manager	Term of Employment
Paul L. Johnson	Sep. 1949 - Aug. 1950
John W. Strothard	Aug. 1950 - Aug. 1951
W. L. Jackson	Aug. 1951 - Sept. 1968
Clyde E. Nef	Sept. 1968 - April 1995
Terry W. Stark	April 1995

Virtually all issues were discussed at meetings of the Board. These meetings were generally quite lengthy. Recommendations were approved by the Board and submitted to the Committee. Since the Committee was made up from members of the Board, the Committee meetings generally followed immediately after the Board and seldom lasted longer than twenty to thirty minutes. The Committee approved the Board recommendations and submitted them to the USDA for review and approval.

The Federal Raisin Marketing Order and its administrative body (the Committee or RAC) came into being during a great challenge to the raisin industry. As has been stated, the raisin industry had developed the capacity to produce more raisins than the war ravaged world could purchase. There was then and is now no question there were many consumers who could and would consume these raisins if they just had the money to purchase them.

Legislation was already in place which would allow industries, such as the raisin industry, to influence the solutions to their problems. Leaders were needed and came forward to propose and implement tools to deal with these problems.

The immediate problem was attacked through, almost single handed, sales of excess tonnage through direct sales to the governments of the United Kingdom and Germany. This solution led to the creation of other challenges.

The solution of one of these challenges was to establish a program of selling reserve pool raisins to packers at a Committee established price for unprocessed raisins. The packers then processed these raisins and sold them into designated export markets. Some packers had challenged the direct sale by the Committee of reserve pool raisins into export markets. With international monetary exchange rates, ocean freight, and import tariffs, the industry concluded a lower price for unprocessed raisins was necessary to sell any significant tonnage in export markets.

Initially there were three pools in the Federal Raisin Marketing Order. The free pool was to supply the domestic and Canadian markets; the surplus pool was to be used to supply export and government needs, and the reserve pool was to supplement the free tonnage, if and as needed. If the tonnage designated as reserve was not needed as free tonnage by April or May of each crop year, it automatically fell into and was disposed of as surplus tonnage.

In 1967 the Order was amended, the reserve pool eliminated, and the surplus pool designated as reserve and only two pools, a free and a reserve pool system established. The free pool continued to provide for the needs of the domestic and Canadian markets and the reserve pool provided tonnage for supplementing the free pool, export markets and government needs. When the Department issued the interpretation in 1976 that both domestic and export markets were to be supplied from free tonnage, the use of tonnage in the reserve pool changed dramatically. Provisions were amended into the Order and programs implemented to utilize reserve tonnage to provide tonnage as needed for free tonnage use, to blend export prices, and to meet government needs.

The initial export program adopted by the Committee made periodic offers of reserve raisins to packers for export to designated markets. These offers were made sometimes as often as weekly, every two weeks, monthly, or longer. Each offer included a specific tonnage, price for the unprocessed raisins, a time period during which the packer must accept the tonnage offered them (generally thirty to sixty days), and a time period during which the accepted tonnage must be exported (generally not more than thirty days beyond the offer period).

The tonnage of each offer was allocated to packers based on their percentage of total acquisitions. For example, if the total industry acquisitions were 250,000 tons and a packer's acquisitions were 25,000 tons, that packer would be offered ten percent of each offer.

The micro-management of the sale of raisins to export markets through small and frequent offers created many requests for change. Packers who were active in selling raisins into export markets quickly committed the tonnage allocated to them and then were forced to withdraw from the market, seek raisins from other packers, or simply wait until the next offer was made. Many importers reported they could not make long term commitments or plan promotion activities because they could not be assured raisins would be available or the price they would have to pay for raisins. If the Committee was really interested in expanding raisin sales in export, they should make larger offers with sales and shipping periods for six months or longer. The Committee implemented this request, but included a clause in each offer that it could be withdrawn without notice if adverse weather occurred during the period of the offer. Tonnage covered by applications filed with the Committee prior to an offer's withdrawal were honored.

The 1976 interpretation by the Department of Agriculture, requiring all markets to be supplied from free tonnage, effectively terminated the Committee's allocation and offer programs for raisin sales to export markets. The Committee's desire to provide raisins for export markets at competitive prices resulted in the development and implementation of the Export Adjustment Offer program, which was subsequently replaced with the 50% Raisin / 50% Cash Adjustment Program, and ultimately a 100% Cash Adjustment Program.

The solution of another of these challenges was the development and implementation of minimum grade and condition standards for both unprocessed (natural condition) and processed (packed) raisins, and an agreement with the Processed Products Branch of the USDA to determine compliance with these standards.

The stories that are told relative to the delivery of raisins prior to the development and implementation of minimum grade and condition standards and third party inspection are almost unbelievable. These standards were not developed and imposed on the industry by the Government or other entity totally unfamiliar with the production and processing of raisins. The Committee members who presented, discussed, developed, and implemented these standards are elected by raisin growers and packers. They also selected the agency to perform the inspection and approve the procedures to be used to determine if a lot of raisins meets the established standards. The Committee recognizes that as long as there is "people judgment" in the inspection process, there will be some variability in the results of inspection. However, there is confidence that the checks and balances in place result in reasonable and acceptable uniformity regardless of the raisin producer or packer whose raisins are being inspected.

The challenge of determining the annual free tonnage trade demand, although possibly still not resolved in the minds of some growers and packers, resulted in the development and implementation of a statistical formula using most recent performance as its base.

As reported in the chapter titled "The Decade of the 1970's" the annual exercise of determining and announcing the annual free tonnage is possibly the most important function of the Committee. This action has a very critical impact on the one hundred percent return to the producer. A tonnage too low can result in increased market prices, reduced shipments, and lost markets. A tonnage too high can result in unreasonable market competition, excessive carryover to the subsequent crop year, and reduced return to producers.

Prior to the late 1970's, the free tonnage was determined by negotiation. Most producers and some packers favored the tonnage being as large as possible. The remaining packers and some producers favored a more restricted tonnage. Experience in 1962 had shown that a limited error in the production estimate resulted in total chaos. The crop, in 1962, was estimated as 148,000 tons and declared one hundred percent free. The crop actually ended up being 168,286 tons and that extra 20,000 tons would impact industry actions and changes for the next two decades.

So intense and boisterous were the discussions on determining and announcing the annual free tonnages that the Department imposed a 24-hour "cooling off" period between the meeting of the Raisin Advisory Board and the Committee at which this issue was considered. As a result, the 1976 amendment proceeding included development and approval of a formula for calculating and announcing the annual trade demand.

Since the calculation and announcement of the annual trade demand takes place before any grapes are laid to dry into raisins, checks and balances in this formula are extremely important. The free tonnage shipments of the prior crop year are used as the base in this formula. An arbitrary reduction of ten percent, and a correction for the physical carryout compared to the desirable carryout is applied to the base resulting in the announced trade demand.

In mid-November, when the production is reasonably known, the tonnage represented by the ten percent reduction in the prior years shipments, plus a tonnage equal to an additional ten percent is offered to packers. No packer is obligated to purchase any or all of the tonnage offered in these two offers, which have come to be known as the 10 + 10 offers.

Minor adjustments have been made in this system of computing and announcing the annual trade demand. The system has worked well and is generally accepted with little controversy.

Merchandising Incentive Programs were developed and implemented to encourage exports of California raisins. These programs have the objective of maintaining and expanding market share. The Merchandising Incentive Program developed and implemented for Japan, has, in the judgment of the Committee, been very successful. Based on this experience, programs have been developed and implemented in other Asian markets; i.e., the ASEAN Countries, Hong Kong, and Taiwan. Importer associations have been organized in each of these markets. Committee delegations have visited these markets and importer delegations have come to California to meet with the Committee. These visits have helped the Committee (industry) to better understand business practices and economic conditions in these markets.

The Committee has developed and offered Merchandising Incentive Programs for many Pacific area markets. Annual target tonnages have been established for each market. If these target tonnages are achieved, through verified export documentation, each importer is paid a cash incentive, plus an advertising/promotion incentive is earned to be used to promote California raisins during the subsequent twelve months. The amount of the cash incentive is increased, if the established criteria for California raisins shipped to the applicable market are met during the period of the incentive program.

The Committee also retains representatives in many foreign market areas who assist in monitoring the imports and use of California raisins. They are able to update the Committee on changes in economic conditions and keep the Committee advised on any political actions or changes in food regulations which may impact raisin imports in the countries they represent. The California raisin industry is faced with the challenges of competition from other producing countries, import country economic changes, monetary exchange and changes in consumers food habits.

The Committee developed and implemented a raisin diversion program. Totally industry funded, this program has never been promoted as a solution to over production of raisins, but rather as a tool to be used only when needed and hopefully for short periods until increased demand can be achieved, or changes in grape production utilization occur to bring supply and demand into better balance.

The annual production of most permanent agriculture commodities is influenced by conditions at bloom and harvest time, and general growing conditions. As a result the annual production of these commodities is reasonably estimable. Such is not the case for raisins. For example, all you can produce from an almond tree is almonds. However, from a Thompson Seedless grape you can produce grapes for fresh use, raisins or wine. Each producer may change from year to year the outlet to utilize his grapes and in many cases can make their utilization decision almost at harvest date.

This ability to change market outlets plus the influence of Mother Nature, especially at harvest time, has resulted in large changes in the production of Natural (sun-dried) Seedless raisins from one year to another. The industry has learned from harsh experience the cost and value of developing and maintaining consumers of California raisins. The cost of storage and maintenance of raisins for a year or more is relatively inexpensive. Sound programs to maintain a supply of raisins to fill demand in low production years have proven very valuable.

As reported in the chapter titled "The Decade of the 1980's" Mr. John D. Pakchoian discussed the Cotton PIK Program with the Manager of the Raisin Bargaining Association and other industry leaders, and the Raisin Diversion Program (RDP) was developed. One of the major points in the development of this Program was, why invest in the production of another crop of raisins when the value of a major part of that crop will not even cover the cost of harvest? Some will and did question why even have a program to keep the grapes in the ground? Let supply and demand eliminate those that can't make it.

At the time the Diversion Program was developed, both the domestic and export markets for raisins were growing. There was also optimism that the wine market would turn around and the demand for Thompson Seedless grapes for crushing would increase. Since the development of a grape vineyard generally takes three years and incurs considerable expense, the industry developed its own self-funded Payment In Kind Program.

This Program, to the outsider, may appear to be a rather complicated program. It is probably not quite as simple as the industry makes it appear. After the diversion tonnage is announced, applications are submitted by producers and approved by the Committee. Successful applicants then remove the vines, if that was their choice, or spur prune off the fruit canes for the next years grape production. If necessary, they may have to go through their vineyard again after the new vine growth comes out and remove any bunches of grapes which may have developed.

Just prior to harvest, generally beginning in June, Committee Compliance Examiners visit each production unit (vineyard) and physically travel through it on ATV four wheeled vehicles, to determine compliance with the provisions of the Diversion Program. If compliance is verified, a tonnage certificate is issued to and traded by the producer the same as if they had produced that volume of raisins.

As stated previously, this is a tool developed under the Marketing Order. It is not a solution, but thus far in the judgment of the Committee, has been a valuable tool.

The fact that a Committee of 47 representatives of the raisin industry has been able to develop and implement these programs is a miracle in itself. The California raisin production area is confined to a relatively small area in the Central San Joaquin Valley. Weather and economic impacts generally are quite similar on all raisin producers.

The Committee's willingness to send delegations to other producing countries, to importing countries, to potential importing countries, to international dried vine fruit producing country conferences, and to meet with USDA representatives has provided opportunities to develop information and intelligence with which to make better judgments and develop and implement industry programs.

The Raisin Marketing Order has been mislabeled as a volume control program. Volume control is incorrect since the program cannot dictate how many raisins any grower can produce. The program should more correctly be called a market allocation program. Its annual objective is to maximize the volume and use of free tonnage. The excess tonnage (reserve) is used to supplement the free tonnage, blend export prices, fill government feeding programs demand, and supplement the supply in short crop years. Each crop year is different and this tool allows the industry to tailor supply with the domestic and export demand.

Commendation is due Committee representatives who serve without compensation. Committee decisions, although limited by the provisions of the Marketing Order, can and do impact the economy of growers, packers, and the area of raisin production.

THE CALIFORNIA RAISIN ADVISORY BOARD (CALRAB)

The administrative body of the State Marketing Order was the California Raisin Advisory Board (CALRAB or Board). When the Marketing Order was implemented, the Board was comprised of fourteen members. It was increased to fifteen members in 1967 to include a representative from the newly established Raisin Bargaining Association, and to sixteen members in 1975 to comply with the State directive to include a public member.

During the existence of CALRAB, there were nine chairmen and seven managers. The early chairmen only served one year terms. However, when I was manager, the terms of office of Board members was two years and the chairman was elected by the Board to serve for the same two year period for which Board members were nominated and appointed. The chairmen and their terms of office and the managers and their terms of employment were as follows:

Chairman	Term of Office
D. R. Hoak	June 1949 - June 1950
C. W. Bonner	June 1950 - August 1951
Walter K. Hines	August 1951 - June 1952
Frank Bergon	June 1952 - June 1953
Henry J. Andreas	June 1953 - June 1955
Dwight K. Grady	June 1955 - June 1956
Henry J. Andreas	June 1956 - October 1964
Dick Markarian	October 1964 - June 1991
Gerald Chooljian	June 1991 - July 1994

Manager	Term of Employment
Paul H. Johnson	June 1949 - August 1952
Norman Katen	Aug. 1952 - March 1956
Gerald Jones	March 1956 - Nov. 1958
Donald White	Nov. 1958 - July 1964
Henry J. Andreas	August 1964 - May 1973
John Calder	May 1973 - August 1977
Clyde E. Nef	Sep. 1977 - July 1994

The primary activities of the State Marketing Order were to fund and administer advertising/promotion and research programs. During its existence, the Board also became involved in food safety issues, international relations issues, and funded Washington, D.C. consultant services.

The activities implemented by CALRAB were funded by assessments on raisin packers and producers. No State funds were provided for this Program. In fact, the expense incurred by the California Department of Food and Agriculture for oversight and enforcement were paid by industry funds collected under the State Marketing Order. From the time the Order was implemented until 1981, all assessed funds were collected by the Department of Food and Agriculture, which also paid all expenses of the Order from these collected funds.

State Legislation was passed in 1980 authorizing marketing order administrative staffs to collect and disperse funds assessed under their program. CALRAB began handling their own funds on January 1, 1981.

From the implementation of the State Order until 1971, the maximum annual assessment rate was $5 per ton, split $2.50 packer and $2.50 producer, or less. These funds limited activity to public relations, development and distribution of recipes, attendance at bakery conventions, and food releases to magazines and newspapers. The Board did become a cooperator with the U.S. Foreign Agriculture Service (FAS) an obtained limited funding for public relations and consumer education in export markets. Foreign representatives were employed to provide market intelligence and assist in the public relations and education activities in their areas.

The first significant change in foreign advertising/promotion activity occurred in the early 1960's with the targeted Japanese market. As stated elsewhere in this book, Mr. Jack Gomperts, a San Francisco exporter, following a visit to Japan, suggested this market offered potential for marketing California raisins. CALRAB investigation found that Western Wheat Associates had implemented a program in Japan to teach Japanese bakers to use wheat flour in their bakeries. Mr. Dick Baum, President of Western Wheat Associates (WWA) was contacted and an agreement signed for WWA to represent California raisins in Japan and to introduce raisins as an ingredient in Japanese baked products. This relationship continued with WWA, which subsequently became U.S. Wheat Associates, until 1990, when the industry decided to expand their activities in Japan beyond bakeries, and Market Makers was contracted to represent California raisins in Japan.

In 1989 a program was implemented to promote the sale of California raisins in consumer packages. This segment of the market had not been addressed and many industry representatives were of the opinion it had potential. After five marketing seasons, this program was discontinued. The Japanese consumer's eating habits and life style are just not conducive to the purchase and use of raisins in consumer packages. It is estimated that in 1998, 95% or more of all raisins exported to Japan are used as an ingredient in a bakery or confectionery product.

The second major change was the increase in annual assessments to implement the recommendations resulting from The Swanson Study.

In 1970 Charles E. Swanson, Ph.D., was contracted by the Board to conduct an Advertising and Promotion Testing Project. This project occurred from January 1970 to April 1971. The results of this study were reported to the Board on May 13, 1971, and the report was also submitted to the Hearing Officer at an amendment hearing on October 13, 1971.

Among other information included in this report, it states that the Board had been operating at the same annual assessment level, of $5 per ton, for the past 13 years -- 1958-1971. During this period the value of the dollar had eroded to a large degree. Specifically, for each $1 spent in advertising in 1958, an expenditure of approximately $2.20 would be required in 1971. Thus, in 1971, the buying power of the Board's budget in terms of promoting raisin sales was approximately 45% of that in 1958. One further way of looking at this picture was that the Board simply was able to purchase less advertising.

Other factors became obvious. Changes in consumer values, attitudes, and habits must be taken into consideration. Women were cooking less and using more convenient pre-processed types of foods. These changing cooking habits certainly were not an asset to the raisin industry, since a recent Industrial/Institutional Market Survey reported food processors did not include raisins in their prepared foods because there was little consumer demand to have raisins included. Further, there was increasing competition for the consumer's dollar from a multitude of other food products. With the consumer becoming less and less aware of raisins, the demand had been decreasing. Without consumer demand, food manufacturers tended to be reluctant to add raisins to their new products.

Three cities, Binghampton, New York; Des Moines, Iowa; and Eugene, Oregon, were selected for testing increased advertising/promotion levels equivalent to a $10 per ton assessment. Approximately 65% of this funding level was directed to full page black and white ads, and one four-color holiday ad in women's magazines such as *Better Homes and Gardens, McCalls, Redbook, Ladie's Home Journal, Woman's Day*, and *Good House-*

keeping. The remaining 35% was directed to two eight-week TV flights: one in September-October, and the other in March-April. These spots were designed to obtain a gross rating point average of approximately 70-80 per week.

The magazine ads appeared in four of the above named six magazines during the months of September, October, November, December, March, and April.

Other cities were selected to test a higher per ton assessment level and yet others selected as a control where no increased advertising/promotion was conducted.

After reviewing and analyzing the data gathered during the entire period of the Test Marketing Program, Dr. Swanson reported "the overwhelming conclusion is that advertising and promotion of California raisins will sell more raisins." After hearing this report, the Board recommended and the Secretary increased the annual assessment rate from $5 to $20.

Market research was done to collect information on who purchased raisins, how often raisins were purchased, how they were used, etc. From this information, target audiences were developed, marketing strategies or messages developed, and timing of "flying" TV commercials approved. Early TV commercials used live actors and were targeted to reach mothers 24-45 years old with young children in the home. Obviously, it was understood that others would also view the commercials, but the message and timing of the commercials were specifically directed to the target audience. As reported elsewhere, the decade of the 1970's was a disaster as far as production of sun-dried seedless raisins was concerned. Prices skyrocketed and yet each year following a production disaster the shipments of raisins recovered dramatically. Much of the credit for this dramatic recovery was credited to the industries advertising, advising consumers that "raisins were back." With the implementation of TV commercials, the industry continued its public relations with magazine and newspaper food editors, and activities with bakery publications, the American Baking Association and the American Institute of Baking.

The industry was successful in selling reserve pool raisins to the Government for use in their feeding programs. A survey was included in one of the school lunch distributions to receive input from users. As a result recipes, storage, and use information was developed and made available to school feeding personnel. CALRAB staff attended national and regional conferences of the American School Food Service Association to obtain information and provide assistance to school feeding representatives.

Following the weather related disasters during the decade of the 1970's and the drastic reduction in the volume of raisin variety grapes annually crushed, the increased production of Natural (sun-dried) Seedless raisins in the decade of the 1980's challenged the industry's ability to market the large volumes of raisins produced. Research conducted by Dr. Swanson and the industry's advertising/promotion activities in the 1970's convinced the industry that usage of raisins could be increased through advertising/promotion.

The expense of twentieth century advertising and promotion vehicles, principally TV, was beyond the industry's ability to totally fund industry approved activities. Although the State assessment had been increased to $65 per ton, split equally between growers and packers, there were still not enough funds to carry out the needed advertising/promotion programs in both the domestic and export markets.

The third major change was the successful efforts of Messrs.

Barserian and Light to obtain government funds for export advertising/promotion activities from the Helms legislation. As stated previously, raisins were the first specialty products commodity to receive such funds. The Helms funds were included in the Farm Bill of 1985 as Targeted Export Assistance (TEA) funds, in the 1990 Farm Bill as Market Promotion Program (MPP) funds, and the 1995 Farm Bill as Market Access Program (MAP) funds. Naturally, the opportunity to obtain these discretionary funds came with terms and conditions. Activities to use such funds could not denigrate other commodities or other foreign produced competitive commodities, all activities and product packaging must identify the product origin as U.S. or California and product distribution must be obtained. Also the industry had to match or exceed the amount of funding provided for these assistance programs.

In most markets, obtaining compliance with these terms and conditions was not difficult. However, for dried vine fruit, the most important importing country in the world, the U.K., California raisins were faced with three major obstacles:

1. The importers contended California raisin prices were too high and the consumer simply would not buy them;
2. U.K. consumers preferred Sultanas and,
3. The retail distribution of consumer packages of California raisins was limited to nonexistent.

The raisin industry developed a TV and print campaign for the U.K. market and introduced it to the importers through meetings of the National Dried Fruit Trade Association. Some packers threatened severing their relationship with their importers if they did not get retail distribution of their brand of raisins. To the absolute amazement of the U.K. importers, the U.K. consumers cleared the shelves of California raisins and requested more from their retail stores. As a result, shipments of California sun-dried seedless raisins to the U.K. went from 5,046 tons in the 1983-84 crop year to 29,992 tons in the 1994-95 crop year. It is interesting to note, the price of raisins shipped to the U.K. also increased from 1983-84 to 1994-95.

With the increased industry assessments, the advertising/promotion activities were expanded in the domestic market and together with government funds such activities were increased in virtually every export market. The results of these and other industry programs surprised even the most optimistic as shipments to the domestic market increased 50 percent and shipments to export markets more than doubled. Even the mature markets of the Scandinavian Countries increased significantly.

The fourth major change was the development and release of the "Dancing Raisins" commercial. As stated previously in one of the industries consumer research programs, the consumer was asked to describe their perception of a raisin. The response to this question was not only depressing but virtual deflation. What value was there to advertising/promoting a commodity with such a negative consumer perception? The challenge was issued to the CALRAB marketing staff and the industry's advertising agency, Foote, Cone, Belding/Honig, to develop a program to modify the consumers' perception of a raisin.

Some time passed and finally a Board Meeting was called to consider the Agency's recommendation. A bit of scene setting is necessary to fully appreciate this presentation. Raisin producers, and to a major degree raisin processors, are part of the last segment of conservative America. In front of this group stood Mr. Seth Warner of Foote, Cone, Belding/Honig. He had removed his blue suit jacket, rolled up his white shirt sleeves, had epaulets on the shoulders of his shirt, kept on his suit vest, had on white tennis shoes and two gold earrings in his ear. A tape of the song "Heard It Through the Grapevine" was played on a "boombox," a colleague held up the commercial story board, and Seth did the hand motions to the proposed commercial. The thirty seconds of this commercial seemed like an eternity. Deathly silence filled the Board room for what was probably only another thirty seconds, but seemed much longer. A Board member said, "Seth, can you do it again?" The tape was rewound and the presentation repeated.

A Board member stated, "It's certainly different than anything we've done before. I move we animate it and put it into testing." This motion was approved. As you look back, there are so many questionables for this commercial. The "claymation" characters were not tried and proven. In fact this was probably the first major exposure for claymation characters commercials. The strategy of the commercial was totally foreign to the raisin industry and made no effort to sell raisins. It was merely entertaining. The cost to develop a thirty second commercial was roughly $300,000 and if it bombed there is no way to recover the cost. Previously used live actor commercials were much cheaper to produce, but if successful, the royalty fees could reach levels comparable to the production cost of this totally untried commercial.

The proposed commercial was animated and tested. Following the testing, the Agency returned to the Board and reported the test results. They weren't sure whether the test results were so far below or so far above commercials with which it was tested that they could give definitive evaluation. In their judgment, the results were above. A motion was made and approved to produce the commercial.

Once produced, copies were made and sent to the TV stations to be shown during the time periods already purchased. No pre-showing, review, etc., was made prior to the commercial being aired. Almost immediately the Agency and CALRAB began getting telephone calls asking when and on what stations the commercial would be shown again. It was quite apparent this was a hit! The Board quickly proceeded to protect the characters through applicable patents and trademarks, and contracted an agency to license their use.

Memorabilia of every type and style using the "Dancing Raisins" was licensed. In fact, a contest was held and three of the original four characters were named. They're Justin X. Grape, Ben Indasun, and Tiny Goodbite. Royalties during the next eight years in excess of $7 million were paid to CALRAB and used for expanding the advertising/promotion activities.

Questions are asked "Did the 'Dancing Raisins' sell more raisins?" The obvious answer is yes, but how much is unknown because there is no way of knowing what raisin sales during this period would have been without them. One sure conclusion is unquestionable. The challenge issued, which resulted in the creation of the Dancing Raisins, has been met beyond anyone's expectations. The consumer's perception of a raisin has certainly been modified. A representative of a competing advertising/promotion agency commented that every agency "would like one of those in their career." That comment certainly compliments the raisin industry for being willing to try something different, take a chance, or stick their neck out. Undoubtedly these comments would be different had this revolutionary commercial bombed.

Agriculture in general, and farming in particular, is most often perceived (there's that word again) as a masculine world. Too often the contribution and support of wives is not recognized. Wives of raisin growers, packers, and others associated with the raisin industry experienced the successes, failures, and economic booms and busts along with their husbands and families. As is quite typical, they wanted to get involved.

A couple of "raisin wives" met with the CALRAB manager and asked, "What can we do?" Many ideas were discussed and very quickly the Raisin Wives were organized and began several programs to promote raisins and the raisin industry. Connie Klein, wife of the then RAC Chairman, Henry C. Klein, was elected the first President of Raisin Wives.

The Raisin Wives organized and conducted an annual Raisin Queen Pageant and dinner. The raisin queens chosen were all college students and represented the industry well at parades, fairs, civic functions, and related industry activities. The Queens all had some relationship to the industry. The first queen, Linda Kay Bedrosian, was the daughter of Krikor Bedrosian, who with his two brothers were raisin producers and also owned and operated a raisin packing plant.

Ten Raisin Queen Pageants were conducted by the Raisin Wives and ten young ladies were chosen to reign as the Raisin Queen for a one year period. Following is a list of the Raisin Queens and their year of service:

RAISIN INDUSTRY QUEENS AND TERMS OF REIGN

Linda Kay Bedrosian	1982-83
Jayne Shapazian	1983-84
Deborah Robinson	1984-85
Suzanne Mosesian	1985-86
Genevieve Sanders	1986-87
Sabrina Harmon	1987-88
Mary Carmelita Jarvis	1988-89
Jane Olvera	1989-90
DeAnn Lewis	1990-91
Susann Bersani	1991-92

The Raisin Wives held a Spring Luncheon and Fashion Show.

At least one year they made a quilt which was given to the lucky winners of a lottery drawing. The author is very familiar with this activity, because he and his wife were the lucky winners. We still have and cherish this quilt.

Each fall the Raisin Wives opened and manned a gift pack store. They developed their own logo and packaging materials. They bought raisins and had them packaged with their own label. Raisin Wives gift packs were purchased and shipped all over the country. They were so successful that many gift pack businesses began operations which reduced the seasonal business of the Raisin Wives to the point they have discontinued their "holiday gift pack store."

The Raisin Wives awarded annual scholarships to college students. These ladies were and are contributors to not only the production, processing, and related industry business, but have contributed significantly to the activities to increase awareness and use of California raisins.

One Queen was invited and accompanied a Fresno delegation to celebrate an anniversary with Fresno's Sister City, Kochi, Japan. Another was invited by the JDFIA to come to Japan and participate in their efforts to introduce consumer packages of raisins in Japan.

Celebrity spokespersons, under agreements with the Board, represented the industry well. These celebrities included Fresno Golfer, Shelley Hamlin; Olympic Gold Medal figure skaters Peggy Fleming and Kristi Yamaguchi; TV personalities Alan Thicke and Tempest Bledsoe, and Arnold Schwarzenegger, as President of the President's Council on Physical Fitness and Sports.

A fitness video featuring Kristi Yamaguchi was developed and released. This video endorses good eating, including raisins and everyone getting involved in an exercise program adapted to individual needs. Each persons physical make up, eating habits, and access to exercise facilities is different. Eating healthy foods and implementing an exercise program adapted to each individual's needs are promoted.

The Dancing Raisins toured major cities in the United States; visited Australia with then Governor George Deukmajian to attend a World Trade Expo; visited Japan to promote consumer packages of raisins; participated in Macy's Thanksgiving Day Parades; participated in lighting activities of the National Christmas Tree, and ultimately were enshrined in the Smithsonian Institute in Washington, D.C. The Dancing Raisins participated in the announcement of the "Puttin on the Ritz" release to Food Editors in the Rainbow Room in New York. They were probably the only non-talking industry visitors to Congressmen and Senators in Washington, D. C.

Newcomers learned and old timers were reconfirmed that what works in one market doesn't necessarily work in another. For example, there were no commercials allowed on the government controlled TV in the Scandinavian Countries. Acceptable vehicles had to be found and used to carry the industry's message. The Dancing Raisins and the commercials developed and used in the domestic market were never really accepted in any export market. The value of in-country employees to assist in development, implementation and evaluation of industry activities in each market area was reconfirmed.

It is doubtful anyone will credit 100 percent of the increase in volume or price to the raisin industry's advertising/promotion efforts. On the opposite side, no one can refute the claim that making the consumer aware of California raisins through advertising/promotion and giving them a chance to make the decision whether or not to purchase California raisins by making them available to consumers in their retail stores, has paid large dividends to the California raisin industry. It has been further interesting to note that at International Sultana (Raisin) Conferences, representatives of dried vine fruit producers from other countries have acknowledged the California raisin industry advertising/promotion activities have increased their sales of dried vine fruit as well.

Reflecting on the industry activities during the 1980's, a number of parts to the puzzle are quite interesting to observe. To obtain Federal funds, the industry was required to be price competitive. The export adjustment programs assured competitive prices. Distribution was required and packers leaned on their importers to be sure distribution was obtained. In country advertising/promotion vehicles were researched and developed to carry the California raisin message to every market. The supply of Natural (sun-dried) Seedless raisins was more than adequate. As a result no demand went unfilled. And finally, the worldwide increased interest in natural foods was really a bonus to the raisin industry.

Early in the 1990's expressions of dissatisfaction with the State Marketing Order traveled through the raisin industry. New packers came into the industry. Some old and other short time packers left the industry. Market price tightened as new packers attempted to enter, other packers attempted to expand and yet others protected their hard earned customers. Unhappiness was expressed with the Credit Back Program. The terms and conditions of this program were opposed by packers who had no "owned" brand to promote, or their processing spread was so tight they did not generate matching funds to qualify for credit back funds. Some packers who marketed virtually all of their raisins in bulk contended they received no value for their assessment funds which were used to promote consumer packed raisins. Other packers contended the severe market price competition gave them insufficient funds to take advantage of the Credit Back Program. Suggestions were made that the Credit Back Program be amended to give back to participating packers 75 or 85 percent of their advertising funds rather than just 50 percent. No amendments to the Program were developed by the Board, and division in the industry grew.

On April 7, 1994, a delegation representing the independent raisin packers delivered a petition to the Secretary of The California Department of Food and Agriculture containing the signatures of 14 packers representing over 50 percent of all California raisins processed, and requested termination of the State Marketing Order for California Raisins. Pursuant to the provisions of the California Marketing Act, the Secretary verified the signatures of those packers on the petition and the volume of raisins processed, and issued an order terminating the Order effective July 31, 1994.

CALRAB WAS NO MORE!!!

As this book was being written, agreement was reached to develop a new grower-only funded State Marketing Order, to be called the California Raisin Marketing Board. Statements have been made that "this new program will be leaner and more focused." Its intention is to improve demand for raisins as an ingredient and in retail packages. Steps toward that goal include touting the health and nutritional benefits of raisins.

Part Three

International Relations

PRODUCING COUNTRIES

During one of his many visits to London to sell California raisins to the U.K., sometime in the mid 1950's, Chairman Setrakian was made aware of the concern of the Australian dried vine fruit industry of the U.S. sales of raisins to the U.K. At that time, Australia was a member of the British Commonwealth of Nations. This membership provided trade preferences to Commonwealth member nations. The Australian dried fruit industry was concerned the U.K. "might become a dumping ground for California raisins."

Prior to 1953, the purchases and sales of all dried vine fruit in the U.K. were controlled by the British Government. This control was released in 1953 and the Australian dried fruit industry expressed their concern to their fellow Commonwealth partner which was also the largest importer of dried vine fruit in the world. Australia was aware they could not supply the full demand for dried vine fruit in the U.K., but they also were concerned with the level of prices created by government "subsidy" payments to dried fruit industries of competing countries, including the United States.

During one of his U.K. visits, representatives of the British Government suggested a visit by a U.S. delegation to Australia may be beneficial and could quiet the fears being expressed. In discussing this suggestion with USDA representatives, the Chairman was advised the Government subsidy payments could not continue indefinitely, and face to face discussions with the then major dried vine fruit supplier to the U.K. could be beneficial.

This matter was presented to the Committee and approval for a delegation of three representatives approved to go to Australia. Questions immediately began relative to why such a trip should be made. At a Committee Meeting held on May 17, 1956, the Chairman responded to these questions. He reported that Australia was a member of the British Commonwealth of Nations; the U.K. market means to the Australians what our domestic market means to us; dried vine fruit sales have been decontrolled by the U.K.; and it is most desirable that we sit across the table and discuss our mutual problems.

The delegation of Messrs. Walter K. Hines, Walter G. Rice, and the Chairman left San Francisco on May 21, 1956, and spent ten days in Australia. In addition to face to face discussions with Australia dried vine fruit representatives, the delegation met the Chairman of the Australian Dried Fruits Control Board, Peter Malick and also Eugene Gorman, who would replace Mr. Malick. Mr. Gorman would subsequently be knighted by Queen Elizabeth, and for the rest of his life, was affectionately known as Sir Eugene.

Sir Eugene, like the U.S. Chairman, was a lawyer. He was regarded as a leading barrister in his country. Like the Chairman, he had retired from the practice of law and spent the rest of his life serving his fellow countrymen. Sir Eugene would spend the next twelve years dedicated to the world dried vine fruit industry. A long lasting friendship between the Australian and California dried vine fruit industries began with this visit of representatives from the California raisin industry to Australia. There is no substitute for personal face to face visits.

It was obvious that Sir Eugene, like the Chairman, was an avid reader. It was a real pleasure for me to listen to Sir Eugene make a point at the International Conferences or discuss issues in private conversation. He had a clear, resonant voice and with his Australian accent and command of the King's English, it was a joy to listen to him.

By 1960 Sir Eugene had visited dried vine producer's organizations in Greece, Iran, Turkey, and the U.S. He was promoting the idea that representatives from these countries should meet together to exchange information and discuss matters of mutual concern, which may be of value to producers of dried vine fruit all over the world.

Prior to the creation of the International Agreement, the practice of vicious, cutthroat competition had put the world Sultana and raisin industry in a chaotic condition. Stability in the world markets was dead. Trade confidence was dead. Prices were at the mercy of buyers and speculators. Something had to be done.

In 1959, Sir Eugene conceived an idea. A daring, bold and exciting idea. He was a man of great knowledge, of great experience and a true friend of dried vine fruit producers all over the world. His idea was to bring representatives of dried vine fruit producers from all producing countries together to exchange ideas and statistics, and to establish an international agreement providing minimum f.o.b. prices as a floor below which no signatory nation would sell it's dried vine fruit. Many of his friends pleaded with him to give up the idea. They said it was impossible. Sir Eugene did not listen.

Sir Eugene met with leaders of Sultana producers in Athens, Ankara, Izmir, and Tehran. The results of these efforts was the first International Conference held in Paris in September 1961, which also included an American delegation. The delegations agreed the world dried vine fruit industries were in a very depressed economic condition, but nothing definite was concluded.

Delegations met again in Rome in April of 1962, and again nothing was concluded. Sir Eugene met with world dried vine producing leaders in each of their countries again and again, crusading for an international agreement. He expressed his opinion to these leaders that such an agreement would place the world dried vine fruit industry on a sound and lasting foundation. It would make it possible for some 600,000 producers to enjoy a reasonably decent return for their sweat and toil. Sir Eugene's efforts were crowned with success.

Representatives from Australia, Greece, Iran, Turkey, and the U.S. met in Athens in June 1963. The seed planted in 1961 "took root and began to grow."

George Papadimitracopoulas, the head of the Greek delegation said, "This Conference has one objective: protection of the producers of Sultanas. All the producers all over the world are depending on this Conference to secure somewhat a better life."

Umit Sanver, the Chairman of the Turkish delegation, eloquently said, "We have 300,000 growers in Turkey. We are working on their behalf. That is all."

Mr. Maleknia, Chairman of the Iranian delegation, said, "Iranian growers pray for the success of this Conference."

Sir Eugene said, "Every man of goodwill in the industry recognizes that the price of Sultanas is too low."

Mr. Setrakian, Chairman of the American delegation said, "The laws of the United States do not permit our industries to enter in agreements which fix prices or allocate supplies to the markets. We repeat what we said in Paris in 1961. We will do everything possible to promote stability, to help any program that will enhance the return to the growers all over the world."

Every delegate attending the Athens Conference knew that the objectives desired could only be achieved by establishing and supporting minimum f.o.b. prices for Sultanas. The idea of putting an end to vicious competition was nothing new. Jim Bishop, the great American author, in his book "The Day Christ Died" states: "The prices of all commodities were fixed by principal officials in Jerusalem. No Jew could undersell a competitor." The world dried vine fruit industry was simply 2,000 years behind the times.

Discussions at the Athens Conference were at times bumpy. The delegates knew they were creating something big. They knew the stability of the world dried vine fruit industry depended on the outcome of this Conference. They were charged with the responsibility of serving their producers. They were "trustees," charged with the responsibility to serve truthfully, unselfishly, and to do everything possible for the producers of their countries. There were times when the delegates did not see eye to eye. They compromised, but they never deserted integrity.

The Athens Conference closed with a minimum f.o.b. price agreement, signed by representatives from Australia, Greece, Iran, and Turkey. Clouds of uncertainty disappeared, trade confidence was restored, and dried vine fruit moved freely in the world markets.

Now, everyone was aware there was no international agency legally in place or available to enforce compliance with this Agreement. Only self monitoring and support could provide the value to such an Agreement.

Annual International Conferences of Sultana (Raisin) Producing Countries have been held almost every year since the original Conference was held in Paris in 1961. In some years, emergency meetings were held to review allegations of violations of the Agreement.

Representatives from Afghanistan joined the Conferences in the late 1960's and up to the early 1980's. Political and other problems resulted in no Afghani representation in recent years.

Representatives from Chile joined the Conferences in the late 1980's.

Representatives from South Africa joined the Conferences in 1968 and South Africa eventually became a signatory to the International Agreement.

Although not signatory to the International Agreement, an

RAC delegation attended all International Conferences until the late 1970's when attendance was prohibited by the USDA. A complaint, the subject of which the industry was never told, resulted in a Justice Department Civil Investigation Demand, and denial of delegations attendance at these Conferences. The CALRAB Chairman and Manager were authorized to attend the 1989 and 1990 Conferences, and an RAC delegation again approved in 1991 and all years subsequent thereto.

Some of the annual International Conferences have been held in producing countries. As a result, representatives from the U.S. have visited every major dried vine fruit producing country except Afghanistan. This has provided an opportunity to observe each country's cultural practices and processing operations. The personal contact with other country representatives has provided a base for dialogue with which the U.S. industry can obtain almost immediate reliable information on crop conditions, etc.

Minutes of the International Conferences have been made available to the U.S. raisin industry, even during the years a delegation was not allowed to attend. These minutes include annual production and disposition statistics provided by each country. They also contain reports of economic conditions of major dried vine fruit consuming countries. The value obtained from the personal contacts of U.S. delegates to these Conferences with delegates from other countries, as well as the personal observations of production practices, is impossible to estimate. The world continues to get smaller. Changes in production or marketing policy of one country can and does have an immediate impact on competitive producing countries.

Representatives of the USDA, AMS, Fruit and Vegetable Division have joined the industry at each International Conference since 1991. All producing countries represented at the International Conferences for the past four years have contributed to a joint dried vine fruit promotion program in the U.K.

The U.S. (California) continues to hold the number one producing country position with their annual production of raisins representing roughly forty percent of the world's annual dried vine fruit production. They are followed in recent years in importance of production by Turkey, Iran, Australia, Afghanistan, Greece, South Africa and Chile.

In a normal year over 85 percent of the dried vine fruit production of Turkey, Afghanistan, Greece, Chile and Iran, and 50 percent of the production of Australia and South Africa is exported. Even though the U.S. is the largest producer, only 30 percent of its annual raisin production is exported. Greece is the major producer and exporter of Zante Currant raisins. Their annual production of Zante Currants is near 40,000 metric tonnes, and the major user of Zante Currants is the United Kingdom.

The recent change in political leadership in South Africa and a change in dried fruit-related policy has resulted in the dissolution of the South African Dried Fruits Board. No central organization controlling the disposition of South African dried fruits continues to exist.

The reduced Sultana production in Australia and the increased wine demand has resulted in some producers replacing their Sultanas with wine varieties of grapes. Short term projections are for continued smaller annual Sultana crops. Whether or not these changes will ultimately impact the continuation of International Conferences remains to be seen.

CONSUMING COUNTRIES

JAPAN

In the summer of 1962 a raisin industry delegation comprised of Walter Hines, Ned Landrum, and the Chairman spent 52 days visiting importing countries in Europe, Scandinavia, the U.K., and a first-time visit to Japan. During their visit to Japan, they met with members of the Japan Dried Fruits Importers Association (JDFIA) and established a long lasting friendship with the JDFIA and its Chairman at that time, Mr. K. Hashimoto. At the time of this visit, the members of the JDFIA represented in excess of 95 percent of all raisins imported into Japan.

It was immediately apparent that business was done different in Japan. Virtually no raisins were imported directly by "end users." Cold breakfast cereals, out-of-hand use of raisins and consumer purchases of raisins for home use were nonexistent. Thousands of small bakeries existed and importers furnished them with flour, sugar, shortening, and other ingredients virtually on a daily basis or at a minimum three times a week. The importers were competitive, but closely knit together in the Importers Association (JDFIA).

Western Wheat Associates, which later joined with the Great Plains Wheat Growers and became the U.S. Wheat Association, had started a program to educate Japanese bakers to use wheat flour. Three master Japanese bakers had been sponsored to the American Institute of Baking in Manhattan, Kansas by Western Wheat Associates. Upon their return, Western Wheat built three portable bakeries mounted on trucks which traveled around Japan teaching local bakers how to use wheat flour in their bakeries.

The California raisin industry was successful in convincing Mr. Dick Baum, President of Western Wheat, to let them join these efforts and include raisins in their education campaigns. A perma-

141

nent institution, the Japan School of Baking, was organized and continues today. They conduct 90-day baking training courses for Japanese bakers. The raisin industry is fortunate to have one full week of this instruction dedicated to baked products using raisins. The benefits from this instruction has many, many times exceeded the raisin industry's contribution to the Japan School of Baking.

Other lessons have been learned by the raisin industry relative to doing business in Japan. Personal visits to Japan are an absolute must. Eye contact, on their "turf," is necessary. Once a relationship is established, Japanese importers are extremely loyal. They expect to be treated fairly and are not unreasonable in these expectations. They are very keen on incentives.

As a result of the raisin industry's education in doing business in Japan, incentives have been established virtually every year since 1963. Annual meetings of representatives of the JDFIA and RAC have been held. At these meetings, information is exchanged relative to changes in the Japanese economy and consumer eating habits, and the California raisin supply situation. Tonnage targets are negotiated and, if reached, an incentive payment of an agreed upon dollar amount per ton of raisins exported to Japan is paid to the JDFIA. In recent seasons the percentage of the tonnage of raisins imported into Japan represented by members of the JDFIA has dropped below 90 percent. Thus incentives paid to the JDFIA are only made on the tonnage documented as exported to JDFIA members. Incentives earned by non-JDFIA importers are used for promotion activities in Japan.

Since the mid 1960's, with the exception of a couple of years, Japan has maintained the position of the number one export market for California raisins. In years of short supply due to adverse weather, the Japanese have imported and used Sultanas and raisins from virtually every competitive producing country. Fortunately they have returned to California raisins when supplies were again adequate. Except in a few isolated instances, California packers have provided the quality and service demanded to maintain this very important market, which now exceeds 25,000 tons annually. Japanese bakers are very demanding in their raisin specifications. Major processing changes have been made by all raisin packers, including putting laser sorters in their processing lines, and yet most raisins are resorted by the bakers in Japan. They would like a zero tolerance for pieces of stems and capstems, if that were achievable.

The California raisin industry employs representatives in Japan, currently Market Makers, to develop, supervise, and evaluate advertising/promotion activities. It cannot be overstated that personal contact in Japan is imperative. In addition to visits by raisin packers and RAC delegations, ongoing contacts by the raisin industry representatives in Japan are necessary and have paid great dividends. Annual baking and new products contests have been and are very popular. The winners of these contests are brought to the U.S. Their visits here include touring the raisin production area and one or more processing plants; meeting with Committee representatives; visits to local bakeries, and for some delegations, a one or two day visit to the American Institute of Baking. The loyalty to California raisins has been far greater than the expense of bringing these bakers to the United States.

The California raisin industry share of the Japanese market naturally suffered in years when the supply was short due to adverse weather. In the years since 1983, with an adequate supply, agreed upon tonnage incentives and continued advertising/promotion programs in Japan, the U.S. share of market has been near or above 90 percent. This has been achieved and maintained with the adjusted export price for raisins exported to Japan, the highest of any export market.

Eating habits of Japanese consumers change very slowly. Use of raisins in cold breakfast cereals, out of hand eating of raisins, and home baking are virtually nonexistent in Japan. Less than 50% of all Japanese homes have convection ovens, so there is very little home baking. The average Japanese housewife shops for food every day, especially for bread, fresh fruit, and vegetables. With the Japanese per capita consumption of raisins at less than one half pound, there is still opportunity for growth. With the hard earned knowledge that the California raisin industry can't just transfer eating habits, etc., from the U.S. to other countries, the impact of the Japan School of Baking and the creativity of Japanese bakers using raisins is needed to further expand the use of California raisins in Japan.

OTHER WORLD MARKETS

Relationships with other world dried vine producing country representatives and the Japanese importers have been covered in some detail. The California raisin industry has gone far beyond just these two areas. Raisin industry delegations have periodically visited with importers and importer organizations in Scandinavia, Germany, Belgium, the Netherlands and the U.K.; in Hong Kong, Korea, Taiwan and Singapore. Other evaluation and survey missions by industry delegations have been made to Vietnam, Hungary, Czechoslovakia, Poland, China, Russia, the Philippines and Spain.

With roughly one third of California's annual shipments of raisins going to export markets, it is impossible to put a price on the value of potential export markets. Who would have thought when Mr. Jack Gomperts told the Chairman, "Now is the time to look into Japan," that in a matter of two or three years, they would become the number one export market and maintain that position for over thirty years. If history repeats itself, who could be the next Japan?

The California raisin industry, as most American agriculture commodities, has been looking to the Pacific Rim markets as future potential growth areas. These countries have significant populations and recent economic growth has been encouraging. As this book is being written, the economic situation in most of these markets is really taking a beating. Hopefully the bottom will be reached quickly and recovery will be achieved. The industry must continue their education and promotion efforts in these markets.

The markets of Europe, Scandinavia and the U.K. are generally looked at as "mature" markets. Consumers in these markets are very familiar with and regularly use dried vine fruit. However, in some markets, Sultanas and raisins are viewed as two distinctly different products. Past experience has proven that, even though mature, there is still potential for growth in these markets. Producers of competitive commodities as well as producers of dried vine fruit in other countries are continually looking to replace California raisins in the consumer's stomach space.

Changes in consumer eating habits probably occur slower than changes in consumers' economy. Education and promotion activities are expensive and competition for consumer stomach space probably at an all time high. Unfortunately when a commodity can least afford to fund education, advertising, and promotion activities, is when such activities are needed the most.

If the Europeans, British, Scandinavians and Asians could only be enticed to adopt the American consumption of cold breakfast cereals, and the Americans adopt the British tea and biscuits or cake consumption, the California raisin industry would be "home free."

SULTANAS/RAISINS

"**A**ll raisins are dried grapes, but all dried grapes are not raisins." That statement appears somewhat controversial until the opportunity is given and taken to investigate the world dried vine fruits and their production methods.

In California the major variety of raisins produced is the Natural (sun-dried) Seedless. This raisin, almost exclusively, begins as a Thompson Seedless grape. The vineyards are generally planted in rows running east to west. The most popular vine spacing is twelve feet between the rows and eight feet between the vines in the row. A stake, generally six or seven feet long, is driven into the ground next to each vine and the vine trained up the stake. A wire is stretched, east to west, along the row of grapes and stapled to each stake.

Thompson Seedless grapes are pruned annually to leave four to six canes, generally, on each vine. When the vine, trained up the stake, reaches a height about a foot below the level of the wire attached to the stake it is cut and a "crown" develops, from which the annual fruit canes grow. These canes, generally two or three in each direction from the vine, are wrapped and tied on the wire which has been stretched east to west along the rows of vines. In recent years some vineyards have been "trellised" by adding a cross arm of twelve to fifteen inches to the stakes and running a wire along each end of the trellis rather than just one wire along the stakes. Hopefully this will give the readers a mental picture of a "raisin" vineyard sufficient to describe the differences in world production methods.

During the growing season the vineyards are irrigated. Some vineyards are flooded (water is run down the vineyard between the rows of vines); some are furrow irrigated (furrows are made

147

next to the rows of vines and the water runs down the furrows), and in recent years many vineyards have had drip systems installed (plastic drip lines are suspended from the grape stakes down the rows of vines and "emitters" installed near each vine). The latest technology is to bury the drip line and emitters underground in the root zone area.

As the grapes near "maturity," generally the last week of July or the first week of August, irrigation is stopped. Temperatures continue in or around 100 degrees Fahrenheit for another four to six weeks. The area between the rows of vines is cultivated to remove any weeds or grass and the ends of the vines which may have grown down and across the area between the rows of vines are cut and disced into the vineyard. Generally one day to a week before harvesting is planned, the ground between the rows of vines has become very dry. At this time this area is "terraced," using an angled blade on the back of a tractor, which leaves the surface smooth and with a slight elevation on the north side of the terrace.

The bunches of grapes are cut from the vines, by hand, and laid to dry on pieces of brown, kraft paper, two feet by three feet, which are called trays, where they remain exposed to the sun for two to four weeks until they become raisins. The moisture content of these completely dried grapes generally averages about ten to eleven percent. The maximum permitted at time of delivery to a raisin packer is sixteen percent.

When the grapes have dried sufficiently, the trays are rolled and remain in the vineyard from one or two days to a week or more. The rolls (bundles) of raisins are then picked up and dumped into wooden bins (4 feet square and 2 feet deep) in which they are stored until processed and packed for the market. Because each grape does not dry at the same rate, the raisins go through a "sweat" in these storage bins where the moisture transfers between the individual raisins and in the vernacular of the industry they "even out."

The Natural (sun-dried) Seedless raisin is generally referred to as dark brown to black. This color is the result of the oxidization and carmellization of the sugars in the grapes as the moisture is extracted by the sun. The skin of the raisins is quite tough so rather heavy washing can occur as they are prepared for market.

In a normal year, 150,000 to 200,000 acres of grapes are harvested to produce raisins. This acreage represents 1,200,000 to 1,600,000 tons of grapes. The harvest is still done by hand and occurs in a four to five week period from roughly the twentieth of August until the twentieth of September. Although the harvest of grapes to dry into raisins generally ends about September twentieth, the trays of grapes may lay out for another thirty days before dry enough to roll and box them. It has been estimated that a labor force of from 40,000 to 50,000 is needed for this short harvest period.

In the dried vine fruit producing areas of Australia, Greece, Iran, and Turkey, the predominant variety of raisin produced is a Sultana.

Although the variety of grape used to dry in some of these countries is called a Sultaninen, or some similar name, it is almost identical to what Californians call a Thompson Seedless.

In some areas of the world, there are no rows of vines. They appear to be planted in a square pattern. They vary from this square planting pattern to other areas where the trellising pattern completely covers the area between the rows of vines. Some areas have no irrigation and others have well developed irrigation systems including drip, sprinkler and sub-surface irrigation systems. The one common practice of foreign production is that the grapes are picked and removed from the vineyard to dry. The one exception to this is that in Australia they cane cut and dry the grapes on the vine for about 10% of their crop.

For purposes of this book, the practices of producing Sultanas in Australia and Turkey will be given in some detail. The practices in other countries, although they may be different, are similar enough that no separate description is included.

In Australia each producer builds drying racks. These racks are generally built in sections roughly fifty yards long. They have ten levels of chicken wire which are each four feet wide. Many growers have sufficient racks to hold about fifty percent of their crop. A grower who normally produces sixty tonnes of Sultanas would require ten fifty-yard sections of drying racks. In the 1950's grapes were hand picked in metal buckets with holes in the sides and bottom to allow the dip solution to drain from the grapes before they are placed on the racks to dry.

In the 1990's the grapes are still hand picked, but the metal buckets (dip tins) are not widely used. The dip tins have been replaced by rack spraying, plastic Bryce buckets and shrub tubs. Since the dipping and spreading of the grapes on the drying racks is so labor intensive, the number of pickers employed by each producer is limited. Each picker picks about 200 buckets per day and the producer's harvest rate varies from 1000 to 3000 buckets per day. Producers who still dip their grapes submerge the bucket of grapes in a dipping solution for one to three minutes before placing them on the racks to dry.

Many producers have gone to rack spraying their grapes. The grapes are hand harvested and spread on the drying racks. They are then sprayed with the dip solution using specially designed, tractor powered booms. The standard strength of the dip solution for both dipping and rack spraying is 25 pounds of Carbonate of Potash and one gallon of dipping oil to 100 gallons of water. It is essential for even colored fruit that the grape berries are completely covered. Partially wetted berries dry at a slower rate.

The skin of a grape is made of overlapping wax platelets (much like fish scales). The dipping solution opens these wax platelets which allows the moisture to leave the grapes more rapidly. Once the drying grapes have reached the desired dryness, they are shaken off the racks by tractor mounted shakers with hydraulically controlled catching trays. The nearly dry grapes are then spread on plastic sheets where they finish drying to the desired moisture of 13% or less. Many growers have mechanical spreaders to place the partially dried grapes on the plastic sheets and also mechanical boxing equipment to pick the dried Sultanas up from the plastic sheets and place them in wooden bins (similar to those used in California) where they are held until processed for market.

It normally takes 10 to 12 days for sprayed/dipped grapes to dry into Sultanas. Australian producers normally put two, and in some years three batches of grapes through their drying racks in a drying season. They usually begin by picking the ripest grapes in their vineyard and as a result produce high maturity Sultanas.

Due to the effect of the dipping solution on the grapes and the short drying period, the Sultanas produced have a straw to golden color. The brighter the golden color, the higher they are graded. One of the negatives with Sultanas is that the effect of the dipping solution on the skin of the grapes allows the Sultanas to rehydrate more rapidly than Natural (sun-dried) Seedless raisins and thus reduces the amount of washing that can be done without re-drying after processing.

Some Sultanas are produced by drying the grapes on the vine. The grapes are sprayed on the vine with a dipping solution which is one-half the strength of that used on rack dried grapes. After the grapes are sprayed, the canes are cut and the grapes dry on the vines. When dried, the Sultanas are mechanically harvested.

Improved grape vines, clonal selection, use of rootstocks, new vine training and trellising, minimal pruning, and upgraded irrigation systems have increased the productive capacity of grapes in Australia. Leading edge growers have doubled the production of their vineyards.

When the author first came into the dried vine fruit industry, Turkish producers dried their grapes in dry yards. The dry yards still exist today, but the composition of those yards has changed dramatically. The early dry yards were made of clay, straw, and in some cases manure. This mixture was sprinkled with water and "rolled down" to make a relatively smooth, hard surface. The grapes were harvested, dipped in a solution very comparable to that of Australia and placed in these dry yards to dry. Once dry, they were raked up, put in burlap bags and delivered to packing houses. Needless to say the drying method and delivery and storage in burlap bags resulted in imbedded capstems and pieces of stem which processing could not remove.

Today the grapes in Turkey are still harvested and dipped in essentially the same way they have always been. However, the dry yards are almost all concrete and a large percentage are covered with plastic before the grapes are laid out to dry. Since most Turkish producers are small, few if any have mechanical equipment to handle large containers. Wood is also a premium in Turkey. Growers who have switched from delivering their Sultanas in burlap bags, now deliver them in plastic boxes which will probably hold 50 to 75 pounds and can be manually handled in preparing and delivering their Sultanas.

After the Sultanas have been processed through mechanical processing equipment, which is virtually the same in every country, the Sultanas are hand sorted, each box of Sultanas is dumped on a table and workers -- generally ladies -- sort through them by hand to remove any foreign material, damaged berries or unwanted dark-colored berries.

In the decade of the 1990's, most Turkish Sultana packers have installed laser scanners in their processing lines which has reduced hand picking by about fifty percent.

Most consumers in Europe and the United Kingdom prefer light colored Sultanas. The changes in cultural practices, harvesting and drying methods, delivery containers and processing methods, is delivering a very acceptable product to the consumer. Several years ago, a large percentage of Sultanas used in the U.K. and Germany were re-cleaned before being used. This is now the case on a limited volume of Sultanas and possibly limited to imports from Afghanistan, Iran and Greece.

Adverse weather during drying never seems to be as devastating to foreign producers. Several factors may contribute to this conclusion. The drying grapes are concentrated in drying racks or dry yards and can be covered to protect them from rain. The harvest covers a longer period and no producer has his entire crop drying at the same time. The drying period is shorter, which reduces exposure time. The most often expressed problem with adverse weather at harvest is production of a darker colored Sultana, which reduces the grade.

GOVERNMENT RELATIONS

The provisions of a marketing order are developed by the industry to which the order applies. They must be considered at a public hearing, approved by two-thirds vote of those who will be regulated through a referendum, published in the Federal Register, and become law. It is the responsibility of the Secretary of Agriculture to determine if the proposed regulations comply with the enabling legislation and if the marketing order is administered within the provisions of the order. All actions of the Administrative Committee (in the case of raisins the RAC) must be reviewed and approved by representatives of the Secretary of Agriculture.

During the existence of the Raisin Marketing Orders, industry delegations have regularly visited USDA officials in Washington, D.C., and government representatives have visited the industry in California. Many of these representatives became well known to Committee and industry representatives. Representatives such as Erwin Graham, Si Smith, Floyd Hedlund, Joe Genske, and George Eastman of the Agriculture Marketing Service, and Fitz Sutherland, Fred Dunn, and Ray McHenry of the Inspection Service were familiar and very helpful to the industry. Ray Russell from the Fresno office of the Inspection Service and Charlie Fuqua of the Marketing Field Office were local representatives with direct oversight of the Marketing Order during its early years.

State representatives Frank Bennett, Jed Adams, Harry Krade, J.D. Rowell, and Dick Gassman represented the Department of Food and Agriculture and oversight of the State Marketing Order.

As the Marketing Orders developed, production and marketing conditions changed and new programs were developed, it was necessary in many instances to hold amendment proceedings to implement changes. The same procedures as establishing a new program had to be followed. Government representatives were very helpful in the development and implementation of these changes. In recent years, government representatives have not been allowed to help industries develop testimony and supporting information for public hearings.

One of the first major amendments was to provide for third party inspection. The horror stories that have been told about grower/packer raisin deliveries are endless. Growers "salted" delivery containers by putting damaged raisins in the bottom and good raisins in the top of the delivery containers. One packer told me his father deducted $2.50 per ton from the payment to one grower and told him it was because his raisins had too much sugar.

The minimum grade and condition standards implemented under the Marketing Order were developed by the industry. The USDA Inspection Service is employed through agreement to sample deliveries from growers and processed raisins at the packing houses to determine if the raisins meet the applicable standards. One inspector tells the story that he was sampling a sweatbox of raisins and found the grower had buried the metal plate used to bolt the rails together on the railroad in the sweatbox of raisins.

Food safety is probably the hottest topic in the food industry as this book is being written. The fact that the raisin industry has adopted grade and condition standards, and employed the U.S. government to perform the inspection for compliance with these standards, has been and is of great benefit. The development of equipment to detect extremely minute amounts of residues raises questions of food safety that didn't exist a very few years ago.

A second issue that the industry became involved with did not involve the provisions of the Marketing Order, but was resolved through relationships established with government representatives. As reported elsewhere in this book, in 1961 a Grape

Crush Marketing Order was established. A major controversy developed between the crush and drying segments of the grape industry. The crush segment wanted to prohibit vintners from purchasing weather (rain) damaged raisins to be used to produce high proof alcohol which is used to fortify wine. The implementation of such a provision could be disastrous to raisin growers.

During a delegation visit to Washington, D.C., the industry representatives were introduced to the Federal Crop Insurance Corporation (FCIC). The FCIC insured many basic commodities, but had not ventured very far into specialty crops such as raisins. Historical information on weather losses of raisins was limited to nonexistent. However, after considerable negotiations, an insurance program was offered for the 1961-62 crop year.

There were virtually no weather related losses in the 1961 or 1962 crop years, and the FCIC was quite pleased with the premium/loss payment ratio. However, Mother Nature struck in 1963 and the loss payments were astronomical compared to the premium income that had been generated. Needless to say, many discussions followed. Another serious harvest time weather disaster did not again occur until 1976. With a longer period of time and less frequent weather disasters, the premium/loss ratio has improved and a program continues to be offered.

The horror stories credited to the insurance program dwarf those of reasons for implementation of the third party inspection program. Since the insurance program is not a part of the Marketing Order program, there has been and is no direct responsibility placed on the Committee for this program. However, there is a direct impact on the supply and quality of raisins produced (in the case of rain damaged raisins recovered) in years of weather damaged crops. High prices, resulting from reduced production due to adverse weather, make it worthwhile to expend funds to recover marketable raisins.

Many adjustments have been and continue to be made in the raisin insurance program. Like many of the programs developed under the Marketing Order, it is a tool. In the judgment of most people in the raisin industry, it is a good tool for those who choose to use it. Misuse of this tool jeopardizes its continuation, and at best, results in the development of safeguards to protect against misuse such as to restrict its real value.

The third program that the Committee has developed as a result of its relationship with government representatives is the Government Feeding Programs. Again during a delegation visit to Washington D.C. it was learned that the USDA has access to funds which may be used to purchase surplus commodities and make them available for Government Feeding Programs. The two sources of these funds are Congressional appropriated and Section 32 funds. The Section 32 funds are generated from import tariffs and must be used for surplus removal programs only. The Congressional appropriated funds can be used to purchase any commodities desired by the users of the Government Feeding Programs.

Most of the raisins purchased by the USDA have utilized Section 32 funds. Raisins purchased by the USDA have been distributed under the School Lunch, Women, Infants and Children (WIC), Needy Persons, and many other government programs. Under these programs the government issues Invitations to Bid to raisin packers. These invitations include specifications for quality, package size, delivery dates, and even the price which the Committee has established at which the packers may purchase reserve pool raisins to fill their accepted bids. I was able to recap sales of reserve tonnage for Government Feeding Programs beginning in November of 1965 which may or may not have been the first such sale. From November 1965 until December 1997, in excess of 227,700 packed tons of surplus/reserve pool raisins have been purchased by the USDA for Government Feeding Programs.

The relationship of the industry, through the Board, with representatives of the California Department of Food and Agriculture have been excellent. All actions of the Board require approval by the State. From the establishment of the Marketing Order until 1981, the State collected all assessment funds and paid all bills applicable to the program.

The Board also developed close working relationships with representatives of the USDA Foreign Agricultural Service (FAS). These representatives were/are responsible for the allocation and oversight of funds the industry has used under the Cooperator, Helms, TEA, MPP and current MAP programs. These funds have been and currently are used in designated foreign markets for advertising/promotion of California raisins.

Agriculture Counselors, Attaches, and Trade Officers in both dried vine fruit producing and consuming countries have been of great value to the Board and Committee. Board and Committee staff members have contacted and continue to contact them during advertising/promotion implementation, compliance and evaluation visits. These representatives in producing countries furnish information applicable to production, distribution, government programs, etc., which is of value to the California industry.

It is difficult to place a value on the industry relationships with government representatives. The U.S. raisin industry is confined to a relatively small space in one state. The fact that this industry has developed and enjoys such positive government relationships is difficult to evaluate. The only hope is that it continues.

160

EPILOGUE

It seems somewhat unreasonable that this chapter may end up being the longest of any chapter in this book. However, there are, in my mind, so many experiences and memories that just don't fit well in any specific segment of this endeavor. Hopefully the readers will read more than just this chapter, but those who have read thus far will also read this final chapter.

Most people who today are in the business which this book attempts to cover, did not live through the conditions which resulted in the creation of the State and Federal Marketing Order Programs. Many undoubtedly question the reasons they were created, and more specifically why they continue to exist. Hopefully this book has correctly reported a period of history, which with some study will help to avoid comparable turbulence in the future. We hear such comments as "What goes around, comes around"; "History repeats itself"; "I'll have to see or do it for myself"; "It will never happen again"; and, "Too soon old, and too late smart."

I realize the risks of identifying specific individuals, since it may fail to include some who correctly justify recognition. However, during the almost fifty years covered in this book, there are some that have left a lasting impression on me, and hopefully are recognized for making positive contributions to the California raisin industry.

My mentor, A. (Sox) Setrakian. Although I only had the privilege of working with Sox for four years, that experience could not have been duplicated. Sox arrived in America penniless. Without detailing more specifics than reported in this book, he conquered adversity and became a successful businessman.

At the time he became a leader in the California raisin and

world dried vine fruit industries, he was past what all of us would identify as the prime of life.

I have heard Sox referred to by many names, many hardly flattering, but one which has long remained in my memory bank was "A benevolent dictator." Sox epitomized a statement he oft quoted from Victor Hugo. "No army can withstand the strength of an idea whose time has come."

At the risk of his health and leaving family and business, he traveled often on behalf of raisin producers. Many of these travels lasted three to four weeks, and one recorded trip was 52 days. Essentially as the result of his tireless efforts and endless pursuits, the California raisin industry has benefited from the knowledge and support of U.S. and foreign government representatives, leaders from competitive country dried vine producers, and foreign importers of California raisins. The recognition of the California raisin industry is the envy of many.

Sox always prepared a written report, many of which included statements which have remained with me. A few are as follows:

"Accuracy is to a newspaper what virtue is to a lady" -- Joseph Pulitzer.

"Get your facts first and then you can distort them as much as you please" -- Samuel Clemens (Mark Twain).

"I have but one lamp by which my feet are guided and that is the lamp of experience" -- Patrick Henry.

"Sometimes we businessmen forget we are now undergoing the greatest test in history of our sense of responsibility" -- Nate Cummings.

"Let us have faith that right makes might; and in that faith, let us, to the end, dare to do our duty as we understand it" -- Abraham Lincoln.

162

"I grow daily to honor facts more and more, and theory less and less" -- Carlisle.

"It is much easier to be critical than to be correct" -- Disraeli.

And finally:

"The time has come for all of us to work together, to pull together, to bury the hatchet in the ground, not in each other, and, God willing, make the grape industry a good industry for everyone" -- A. Setrakian.

Through Sox's leadership and the support of the raisin industry, positive relationships with the representatives of the U.S. Department of Agriculture, foreign dried vine fruit producers, and foreign importers (especially the Japan Dried Fruit Importers Association) were developed and have continued.

Sir Eugene Gorman and the Australian Dried Fruits Control Board. Even with his friends telling him his efforts to gain cooperation among the dried vine fruit producing countries of the world would not be successful, Sir Eugene would not give up. As a result of his efforts, these countries continue to meet annually to exchange production and marketing statistics. The personal contacts have been, and are valuable beyond most people's realization.

The Australian Dried Fruits Control Board has served as the convener of the Annual International Conferences. This has been an awesome task since no two Conferences have been held in the same location. Other than about six years, when Sox served as the Chairman, the Chairman of the Australian Board has served as the International Conference Chairman. They have earned the gratitude of the world dried vine fruit industries.

Ernest Bedrosian was a young upstart in the mid 1960's. Ernie had demonstrated his desire to improve the economic life of grape and raisin growers through his service on the Grape Crush and Raisin Administrative Committees. Undoubtedly there were many others involved, but Erniᴇ is credited with being the father of the Raisin Bargaining Association.

In the mid 1960's, Sox suggested organizing a bargaining association to an industry delegation during a visit to Washington D.C. By 1966 this suggestion had grown to the point that Ernie started and lead the campaign which ultimately resulted in the establishment of the Raisin Bargaining Association. Organization meetings, grower district meetings, establishment of target tonnages for activation, sign up of growers, and development of bylaws, etc., occupied many hours. Finally in February of 1967, the targets had been met and the RBA was made effective.

Ernie was elected as the first president of the RBA. With other officers and a board of directors, an office was opened, staff employed, and efforts directed to obtain signatory packers and development of procedures for price negotiations undertaken. The annual tonnage of Natural (sun-dried) Seedless raisins represented by members of the RBA would exceed 40 percent of total production.

Kalem Barserian and Frank Light were mild to strong antagonists toward each other during their early respective careers with the Raisin Bargaining Association and Sun Maid Growers. I am not aware of what brought down the barriers between these two, but I am quite aware of the results of their working together once those barriers were removed. Many of their accomplishments are undoubtedly omitted, but a few are noted.

The annual "free for all" to agree on the free tonnage was ended and a formula adopted to compute and announce the annual trade demand. Amendments to the Marketing Agreement Act were made to include raisins in Section 608(e) to require dried vine fruit imports to meet minimum grade and condition standards. A Section 301 case was filed under the General Agreement on Tariffs and Trade challenging the subsidy practices of foreign grape producing countries which adversely impacted the California grape and raisin industries. The 1984 Raisin Price Adjustment and Free Tonnage Inventory Adjustment Programs were implemented. These two programs were devastating upon implementation, but ultimately doubled export volume and increased domestic volume by fifty percent. Raisin grower prices increased quickly following the severe adjustment prices to reach generally acceptable levels by the late 1980's.

The raisin industry became the first special commodity industry to receive USDA discretionary funds for advertising/promotion activities in export markets. During their tenure, the assessment funds for advertising/promotion were significantly increased, the packer credit back program was implemented, delegations visited potential export markets, and the "Dancing Raisins" were created.

John D. Pakchoian suggested and became the father of the Raisin Diversion Program. The idea for this Program came from John's service on the Fresno County ASCS Committee which administered the Federal funded cotton Payment in Kind Program. Other growers and industry representatives were very involved in development of the detail of this program. The raisin industry's Diversion Program was and is self funded with reserve pool income and uses no government funds.

It is impossible to list all of the representatives of foreign producing countries, importers, and State and Federal governments, Committee and Board members, foreign representatives and exporters who have played a role in the activities of the California raisin industry during the decades of 1950 through 1990. With all of the experiences of these 47 years, one wonders if

165

they have seen them all. I suspect the comments of a long time Sun Maid Controller at the time of his retirement would be more correct: "I haven't seen next year yet!"

Although included in the Epilogue section of this book, this part may be more appropriately called an Epitaph. Changes in ownership, ending operations, and beginning new operations have resulted in many changes in raisin packers during the period covered by this book. It has been interesting to note that the number of packers operating in any given crop year has remained very near the number 20, even considering all of these changes.

In crop year 1997-98 only seven packers are still in operation who were operating when the Marketing Orders were implemented in 1949. Eleven packers operating in 1949 have ceased operations. Two packers who were operating in 1949 have changed ownership once or more and are still operating. Six packers began operations and subsequently ceased to operate during the period covered by this book. One packer began operations and has changed names and/or ownership five times.

Some packers have developed regional or limited national distribution of their own brand of raisins in consumer packages. Only one brand, Sun Maid, is distributed and recognized in national and international consumer dried vine fruit markets in 1998.

APPENDIX

Natural (Sun-dried) Seedless Raisins

Sweatbox Tons

Crop Year	Production Tons	Free Tonnage Tons	Grower Price $	Reserve Tonnage Tons	Grower Price $	Grower 100% Return
1950-51	127916	127916	260.00	-0-	-0-	260.00
1951-52	211125	164678	162.50	46447	158.15	161.54
1952-53	242127	179186	158.58	62941	130.09	151.16
1953-54	204282	165468	159.65	38814	126.41	153.34
1954-55	143991	118548	176.97	25443	111.41	165.39
1955-56	194076	155261	170.36	38815	130.88	162.46
1956-57	174827	146752	189.36	28075	177.54	187.35
1957-58	138888	138888	263.00	-0-	-0-	263.00
1958-59	134549	134549	311.00	-0-	-0-	311.00
1959-60	198745	142171	210.05	56574	143.73	191.15
1960-61	170264	148128	214.31	22136	194.39	211.72
1961-62	205554	151715	216.64	53839	157.16	201.06
1962-63	168286	168286	266.00	-0-	-0-	266.00
1963-64	195368	149455	250.59	45913	206.76	240.29
1964-65	209903	144443	251.31	65460	196.56	234.20
1965-66	243303	134684	252.28	108619	152.07	207.51
1966-67	259072	139823	233.75	119249	165.58	202.38
1967-68	161320	143751	305.00	17569	175.20	290.72
1968-69	240949	138548	312.50	102401	187.68	259.45
1969-70	227429	131913	317.50	95516	183.74	261.32
1970-71	176066	123246	320.00	52820	181.07	278.32
1971-72	172347	132707	325.00	39640	298.83	318.98
1972-73	91258	91258	500.00	-0-	-0-	500.00

Natural (Sun-dried) Seedless Raisins

Sweatbox Tons

Crop Year	Production Tons	Free Tonnage Tons	Grower Price $	Reserve Tonnage Tons	Grower Price $	Grower 100% Return
1973-74	198753	198753	700.00	-0-	-0-	700.00
1974-75	212390	155045	640.00	59345	510.58	605.06
1975-76	253271	151963	647.50	101308	545.72	606.79
1976-77	117605	117605	1050.00	-0-	-0-	1050.00
1977-78	218813	150982	840.00	67831	890.12	855.54
1978-79	74410	74410	1600.00	-0-	-0-	1600.00
1979-80	263108	186807	1150.00	76301	1184.10	1159.89
1980-81	254659	170620	1200.00	84037	1099.00	1166.67
1981-82	224463	179570	1295.00	44893	1051.59	1230.32
1982-83	205700	205700	1300.00	-0-	-0-	1300.00
1983-84	347943	130479	1300.00	217464	136.67	572.92
1984-85	299473	182679	700.00	116794	415.12	588.90
1985-86	362657	213968	801.00	148689	281.57	593.34
1986-87	346944	228983	885.00	117961	491.57	751.23
1987-88	352498	236176	951.00	116324	533.30	813.16
1988-89	379053	265337	1025.00	113716	663.50	916.55
1989-90	395501	288716	1115.00	106785	641.04	987.03
1990-91	357249	246502	1115.00	110747	353.91	879.06
1991-92	352659	278601	1155.00	74058	238.10	962.45
1992-93	371516	263776	1155.00	107740	280.54	901.41
1993-94	387007	286385	1155.00	100622	191.92	904.60
1994-95	378427	291389	1160.00	87038	152.48	928.27
1995-96	325911	257470	1160.00	68441	432.35	1007.19
1996-97	272063	233974	1220.00	38089		

Raisin Variety Grape Production and Utilization

Crop Year	Production Green Tons	Crushed Green Tons	Dried Green Tons	Fresh & Canned Green Tom	Natural (Sun-dried) Production Dry Tons
1950-51	1331300	538700	624000	168600	127916
1951-52	1808300	653400	968000	186900	211125
1952-53	1653300	302700	1152000	198600	242127
1953-54	1514300	378900	932000	203400	204282
1954-55	1247300	373800	672000	201500	143991
1955-56	1709300	567800	900000	241500	194076
1956-57	1617300	554700	836000	226600	174827
1957-58	1372300	485800	652000	234500	138888
1958-59	1630300	660500	744000	225800	134549
1959-60	1827300	599700	971000	256600	198745
1960-61	1695000	603900	848000	243100	170264
1961-62	2048000	720000	1075000	253000	205554
1962-63	1707000	648000	789000	270000	168286
1963-64	2193000	871000	1069000	253000	195368
1964-65	2020000	701000	1033000	286000	209903
1965-66	2575000	979000	1295000	301000	243303
1966-67	2175000	675000	1184000	316000	259072
1967-68	1635000	615000	751000	269000	161320
1968-69	2135000	709000	1110000	316000	240949
1969-70	2155000	845000	1007000	303000	227429
1970-71	1871000	851000	820000	200000	176066
1971-72	2312000	1204000	893000	215000	172347
1972-73	1344000	717000	436000	191000	91258
1973-74	2376000	1210000	967000	199000	198753
1974-75	1970000	754000	1021000	195000	212390

171

Raisin Variety Grape Production and Utilization (cont'd.)

Crop Year Green Tons	Production Green Tons	Crushed Green Tons	Dried Green Tons	Fresh & Canned Green Tom	Natural (Sun-dried) Production Dry Tons
1975-76	2201000	729000	1249000	222400	253390
1976-77	2250000	755000	1274000	221000	117605
1977-78	1935000	594000	1132000	209000	218813
1978-79	1918000	702000	1006000	210000	74410
1979-80	2320000	700000	1376000	244000	263108
1980-81	2690000	780000	1618000	292000	254657
1981-82	1779000	509000	1024000	246000	224463
1982-83	3062000	774000	1530000	338000	205700
1983-84	2535000	330000	1774000	287000	347943
1984-85	2282000	587000	1390000	305000	299473
1985-86	2487000	559000	1557000	371000	362657
1986-87	2045000	505000	1180000	360000	346944
1987-88	2170000	440000	1430000	300000	352498
1988-89	2570000	415000	1810000	345000	379053
1989-90	2570000	370000	1850000	350000	395501
1990-91	2345000	270000	1750000	325000	357249
1991-92	2165000	284000	1562000	319000	352659
1992-93	2670000	785000	1551000	334000	371516
1993-94	2410000	453000	1642000	315000	387007
1994-95	2389000	197000	1884000	308000	378427
1995-96	2252000	432000	1532000	288000	325911
1996-97	2186000	618000	1302000	266000	272063

Bearing Acreage

Crop Year	Total	Wine	Table	Raisins	Grape Production	Natural (sun-dried) Seedless
1950-51	496,639	165,006	93,685	237,673	2,432,000	127,916
1951-52	480,834	158,058	91,329	231,467	3,219,000	211,125
1952-53	463,510	154,158	86,002	223,350	2,958,000	242,127
1953-54	454,096	146,203	83,953	223,940	2,473,000	204,282
1954-55	445,522	139,091	82,524	223,907	2,327,000	143,991
1955-56	423,774	136,119	80,519	207,136	3,020,000	194,076
1956-57	407,507	128,510	76,191	202,806	2,641,000	174,827
1957-58	399,000	120,469	75,327	203,204	2,382,000	138,888
1958-59	406,847	118,998	78,042	209,807	2,741,000	134,549
1959-60	409,101	117,185	78,962	212,954	2,857,000	198,745
1960-61	416,180	118,072	80,937	217,171	2,694,000	170,264
1961-62	424,876	116,393	81,772	226,711	2,804,000	205,554
1962-63	444,146	120,008	84,130	240,008	2,928,000	168,286
1963-64	451,496	121,341	82,651	247,504	3,350,000	195,368
1964-65	454,922	120,060	83,373	252,489	3,155,000	209,903
1965-66	459,850	123,010	83,660	253,180	3,975,000	243,303
1966-67	461,640	126,200	82,060	253,580	3,400,000	259,072
1967-68	458,280	125,650	81,270	251,360	2,700,000	161,320
1968-69	456,170	128,260	78,100	249,810	3,255,000	240,949
1969-70	457,270	132,470	74,230	250,570	3,595,000	227,429
1970-71	447,920	131,800	70,770	245,350	2,763,000	176,066
1971-72	445,860	133,970	68,090	243,800	3,534,000	172,347
1972-73	443,430	137,210	65,830	240,390	2,266,000	91,258
1973-74	455,230	149,360	66,610	239,260	3,887,000	198,753

Bearing Acreage (cont'd.)

Crop Year	Total	Wine	Table	Raisins	Grape Production	Natural (sun-dried) Seedless
1974-75	489,570	181,840	66,900	240,830	3,789,000	212,390
1975-76	526,190	225,160	63,130	237,900	3,948,000	253,271
1976-77	576,030	277,800	62,330	235,700	3,978,000	117,605
1977-78	621,726	315,175	64,333	242,218	3,986,000	218,813
1978-79	616,247	313,654	62,245	240,348	4,017,000	74,410
1979-80	602,841	301,514	61,554	239,773	4,558,000	263,108
1980-81	596,630	290,686	62,506	243,438	5,124,000	254,657
1981-82	592,081	278,935	63,480	249,665	3,993,000	224,463
1982-83	619,976	291,413	67,783	260,780	6,138,000	205,700
1983-84	644,513	300,644	72,041	271,828	4,907,000	347,943
1984-85	675,000	317,000	77,400	280,600	4,480,000	299,473
1985-86	681,957	320,782	77,725	283,450	5,203,000	362,657
1986-87	670,823	312,320	81,620	276,883	4,770,000	346,944
1987-88	661,400	304,100	82,800	274,500	4,660,000	352,498
1988-89	653,700	298,900	84,100	270,700	5,485,000	379,053
1989-90	641,700	290,000	80,700	271,000	5,390,000	395,501
1990-91	639,000	291,000	78,000	270,000	5,185,000	357,249
1991-92	635,500	294,000	75,500	266,000	4,980,000	352,659
1992-93	644,300	300,000	77,300	267,000	5,460,000	371,516
1993-94	655,800	312,000	77,800	266,000	5,383,000	387,007
1994-95	654,800	307,000	77,800	270,000	5,256,000	378,427
1995-96	646,800	302,000	76,800	268,000	5,234,000	325,911
1996-97	655,500	311,000	74,500	270,000	5,003,000	272,063

Natural (Sun-Dried) Seedless Raisin Shipments

Packed Ton

Country of Destination	Crop Year 1959-60	Crop Year 1967-68	Crop Year 1975-76	Crop Year 1982-83	Crop Year 1989-90	Crop Year 1996-97
Denmark	4355	4079	2465	1797	5983	5853
Finland	1792	3897	2550	939	2605	2483
Germany	3424	2621	2402	2821	13002	8805
Netherlands-	3614	874	2149	1319	3517	2793
Norway	2537	2353	1838	969	2644	2608
Sweden	5123	4669	3552	2640	6150	5423
U. K.	15489	11844	7295	2433	23996	27688
Other Europe	5816	3261	1515	1091	3233	3186
Hong Kong	399	653	431	718	694	1445
Japan	1570	19628	21546	19332	25745	28822
Korea	- 0 -	- 0 -	241	2402	4714	2814
Singapore	- 0 -	- 0 -	- 0 -	523	1030	2594
Taiwan	- 0 -	1044	1137	3700	3305	3918
Others	148	4570	2451	2940	2335	7236
Latin America	3646	3637	1868	2473	1961	4046
Total Exports	47913	63130	51440	46097	100914	109714
Domestic & Canada	119557	123524	131652	147489	205279	184692

175

Natural (Sun-Dried) Seedless Raisin

Crop Allocation and Grower Return

Note the reserve pool was deleted in 1967 and the surplus pool renamed reserve

Crop Year	Free Tonnage		Surplus/Reserve Tonnage		100% Grower Return
	%	$/Ton	%	$/Ton	$/Ton
1950-51	100	260.00	- 0 -	- 0 -	260.00
1951-52	65	162.53	35	159.71	161.54
1952-53	55	157.66	45	143.24	151.17
1953-54	61	160.00	39	142.92	153.34
1954-55	82	176.99	18	112.56	165.39
1955-56	65	170.10	35	148.26	162.46
1956-57	73	189.40	27	181.81	187.35
1957-58	100	263.00	- 0 -	- 0 -	263.00
1958-59	100	311.00	- 0 -	- 0 -	311.00
1959-60	68	210.42	32	150.19	191.15
1960-61	74	212.59	26	209.23	211.72
1961-62	65	215.26	35	174.69	201.06
1962-63	100	266.00	- 0 -	- 0 -	266.00
1963-64	60	250.00	40	225.73	240.29
1964-65	60	250.00	40	210.50	234.20
1965-66	45	250.00	55	172.75	207.51
1966-67	50	232.31	50	172.24	202.38
1967-68	89	305.00	11	175.20	290.72
1968-69	57.5	312.59	42.5	187.68	259.45
1969-70	58	317.50	42	183.74	261.32
1970-71	70	320.00	30	181.07	278.32
1971-72	77	325.00	23	298.83	318.98
1972-73	100	500.00	- 0 -	- 0 -	500.00

Crop Allocation and Grower Return (cont'd.)

Crop Year	Free Tonnage		Surplus/Reserve Tonnage		100% Grower Return
	%	$/Ton	%	$/Ton	$/Ton
1973-74	100	700.00	- 0 -	- 0 -	700.00
1974-75	73	640.00	27	510.58	605.06
1975-76	60	647.50	40	545.72	606.79
1976-77	100	1050.00	- 0 -	- 0 -	1050.00
1977-78	69	840.00	31	890.12	855.54
1978-79	100	1600.00	- 0 -	- 0 -	1600.00
1979-80	71	1150.00	29	1184.00	1159.89
1980-81	67	1200.00	33	1099.00	1166.67
1981-82	80	1275.00	20	1051.59	1230.32
1982-83	100	1300.00	- 0 -	- 0 -	1300.00
1983-84	37.5	1300.00	62.5	136.67	572.92
1984-85	61	700.00	39	415.12	588.90
1985-86	59	810.00	41	281.57	593.34
1986-87	66	885.00	34	491.57	751.23
1987-88	67	951.00	33	533.30	813.16
1988-89	70	1025.00	30	663.50	916.55
1989-90	73	1115.00	27	641.04	987.03
1990-91	69	1115.00	31	353.91	879.06
1991-92	79	1155.00	21	238.10	962.45
1992-93	71	1155.00	29	280.54	901.41
1993-94	74	1155.00	26	191.92	904.60
1994-95	77	1160.00	23	152.48	928.27
1995-96	79	1160.00	21	432.35	1007.19
1996-97	86	1220.00	14	NA	NA
1997-98	66	1250.00	34	NA	NA